What D

Secular Theology

Stephen Gratwick QC was educated at Charterhouse and Balliol College, Oxford. After graduating in physics and electronics, he worked for two and a half years in electronics research for the Government during the Second World War.

As a lawyer, Queens Counsel and Bencher of Lincolns Inn, he spent over 40 years practising in Intellectual Property, primarily on scientific patents.

He lives in the south-east of England with his wife, Jocelyn.

What Does God Do?

Secular Theology

Stephen Gratwick

Haymist Press

First published in 2009 by
Haymist Press
14A Kippington Road
Sevenoaks, Kent
TN13 2LH

© 2009 Stephen Gratwick

A CIP Record for this book is available from
The British Library Cataloguing Data Office

ISBN: 978 0 9561998 0 5

Designed and typeset by
Columns Design Limited, Reading
Printed and bound in Great Britain by
TJ International Ltd

Contents

Acknowledgement

My grateful thanks go to David Burnett without whose
encouragement and assistance this would still be
only bytes on a hard drive
and
to David Babb who has turned those bytes into this book

Preface

There has long been a dispute as to whether science is in conflict with religion. There are those, such as Professor Richard Dawkins, author of *The God Delusion*, who maintain that there is such a conflict and who are somewhat aggressive in their attitude to religion. Then there are those, such as Professor Russell Stannard, author of *The God Experiment*, who think that there is no such conflict and who are firm believers in their religion. Then there are many, such as the philosopher David Hume, who have subjected the position of religion in our culture to much study.

That is an unproductive dispute and seldom looks at the considerations which really need to be addressed. The historical fact is that, over the centuries, secular knowledge about our Universe, and ourselves as part of that Universe, has grown; and it is growing ever more rapidly as the years pass.

What is required today is to examine the nature and propositions of theology and to compare them with the secular facts which we now know. Many of those facts have emerged because of the work of scientists. But that does not make them something separate to be called 'science'. They are facts and the question is, or should be, which, if any, of the supernatural propositions of religion can co-exist with the verified secular facts.

There is much talk in the media these days about the decline in Christian values. Much of what is said discusses secular matters such as courtesy, binge drinking and knife fights. There is also mention of the decline in such matters as churchgoing and marriage. There is concern about the growth of Islam in the UK and the manner in which it is regarded; about multiculturalism; about women as priests and bishops; and about homosexuality, especially in the Anglican Church.

There is, in truth, a confused cacophony of secular and theological arguments surrounding us with no clear recognition of the enormous growth in the knowledge of our Universe, and ourselves in it, and of the impact of that knowledge on theological concepts which have hitherto been taken for granted.

In addition, and certainly no less important, is the growth in globalisation. Today, we are more aware of the large number of different cultures in the world, and the existence of religions other than those based on a belief in Jesus Christ.

The underlying thesis of this book is not a new one. You will find discussions of such matters as far back as the eighteenth century in the works of David Hume. You can read more in the works of other philosophers such as John Stuart Mill, novelists such as George Eliot, and even Darwin himself. But they are all rather heavy going.

My aim is to elucidate some aspects of that knowledge which are relevant to the existence and nature of gods, God and religion; to invite a reassessment of some of the topics with which theology deals and of some of the topics involved in comparative theology; and to do so in a way which can easily be understood, but without being superficial.

Introduction

The question in the title is not as to whether God ever did anything in the past. He may well have created the Universe as everyone of any religious persuasion believes. That is a topic about which I have something to say later.

The question which the title asks is whether He should be regarded as doing anything in the here and now.

It is a historical fact that, in the past, much that happened in the world was considered by theologians to be the result of God's daily activities. More recently, it has been thought, especially by most scientists, that there is a secular explanation for much of what happens.

So, let us look at the meanings of the words 'theology' and 'secular' and examine what the differences really are. I use the Shorter Oxford English Dictionary.

According to the SOED, theology is

> 'The study or science which treats of God, His
> nature and attributes, and His relations with
> man and the universe.'

This definition assumes monotheism but the dictionary adds the words: 'applied to pagan or non-Christian systems'.

It is, of course, the fact that no theologian studies God because he cannot do so. What is in reality involved in theology is discussion and debate among mankind of mankind's ideas about God and other religious matters. In fact, what the theologian studies is the sacred texts of the religion under study, and the published views of those who have studied such matters.

There is a large number of topics involved in a study of a religion, and I shall attempt to address many of them. However, what I aim to do, in respect of each topic, is to draw attention to secular considerations which are related to that topic. Many such considerations have come to light over the last few centuries but the theologians do not always take them into account. I do not aim to be confrontational: nor assertive in the manner of a Dawkins or Hitchens. What I hope to do is to place side by side secular and theological considerations and concepts so that the reader cannot escape the need to make up his own mind.

To what extent such an exercise will influence those who wish to believe in the existence of God and His activities is problematical. Many such people struggle hard to avoid having to come to a conclusion against the existence and activities of God. Frequently they proceed by posing a question to which there is no known answer; or stating a proposition for the cause of which there is no known explanation. Such a line was taken by the Chief Rabbi in *The Times* of 30th August 2008.

Such conduct constitutes a defensive tactic. One can read the whole of such theses and find no rationalisation of God's contribution to the topic in question. In many of such cases, one finds that something, or some step, attributed to God was so attributed because the relevant facts had not yet been discovered. Perhaps the best known example of that is seen in what happened to Galileo. In the course of this book you will come across many more examples of attribution to God being displaced by recognition of a secular understanding of what is involved.

Now I move on to the word 'secular'. The SOED has much to say, but this seems to be the most relevant

'Belonging to the world and its affairs as distinct from the Church and religion'.

Much of what has been discovered by scientists is secular as opposed to theological, but it is a mistake to suppose that the two terms have no meeting ground.

In what follows I shall hope to persuade you that much of what is accepted as theological truth is thought to be such because those concerned have not faced up to the difficulties with which secular knowledge confronts the mind.

Here is another important consideration. In one respect, there is a fundamental difference between secular and theological considerations. Secular views are continually being added to as more and more is learned about the Universe and us who live in it. No such source of religious knowledge is available to the theologian because the essence of that which he studies is material which was set in stone in sacred texts a long time ago.

This distinction manifests itself most often when theologians point to concepts which have not, that is to say 'not yet', become the definitive fruit of secular studies. As I shall show, there are many instances in the past of theological views being changed in the light of secular discoveries. What needs never to be forgotten is that this process of enquiry, study and ascertainment has not stopped and will not stop. So he who says that the secularist has no answer should always add the word 'yet'.

1

The Search for Understanding

Before one can start discussing theology, it is necessary to have a look at its basis; that is to say at the idea that there might exist such a thing as a god. You will not see one as you look out of your window, or walk about the streets. Some people claim to have had visions but, for most of the human race, gods are invisible. Yet many people are convinced that a God, or gods, exist. So it is not a bad idea to ask why.

There is much dispute among the learned as to how and when humankind conceived the idea that there exist gods. In the past there were many, many gods. As of today, most of the human race seems to harbour the idea that gods exist; but there are comparatively few gods in the major religions. Many religious people adhere to a single god.

It has been suggested that humankind has a genetic propensity to 'fall in love' and that this has survival value because it conduces to better care for the upbringing of the next generation. From that it has been suggested that the propensity to be religious has the same root. However, that seems to be concerned more with why religion has persisted and does persist, than with explaining why mankind thought up the idea of gods in the first place.

For what it is worth, here are my own thoughts. They may not appeal to evolutionists or theists or philosophers. Nor is it important whether I am right or wrong. What is important is that what follows draws attention to some of the things which have puzzled mankind for a long time; and to the progress which he has made in solving those puzzles.

It is clear from all the work of archaeologists that mankind has, for a very long time, regarded his world as governed by gods.

Looking back, this is not a matter for surprise. He had a brain which asked questions and looked for answers. He found himself in a world which was so complex that he had difficulty in understanding things. There was land and water; the sky above; the sun, moon and stars; the seasons; the vagaries of the weather; the animals, the birds and the fishes; the trees, the grass, the fruits, the nuts; and himself.

Many of these things appeared to obey rules: to be predictable. Water would always run downhill. The moon appeared with great regularity and went through a series of phases: he learned their sequence and became quite skilled at predicting what the moon would do from past experience of what it had done. The seasons, especially in temperate climates, followed a pattern. Again, he could predict. Later on he learned that there was a proper time to plant seeds and that planting at other times was likely to be an unrewarding experience. He learned that, if he planted seeds in the 'right' way and at the 'right' time, plants would grow; and then he could harvest.

Somewhere, somewhen, came the idea that all these things were under the control of powerful invisible beings. It is an idea which cropped up in many parts of the world: if not everywhere. Such beings were called gods.

There was nothing in the world which he perceived with his five senses to tell him how the world in which he lived, and he himself, came to be; nor what caused things to happen as they did. It was the business of the gods to be responsible for, and control, these phenomena which he himself could not control, and which he did not understand.

The number of such gods is very large. There were the pantheons of the Pharaohs, the Greeks, the Romans, and the Norsemen. There were other individual gods, whose names are commonly known, such as Baal, Moloch, and Mithras and there are the gods of the Aztecs, the Incas and the Maya. Roman Emperors claimed to be gods: what did they mean by that? Not least there were, and are, the gods of the Jews, the Christians, the Muslims and the Hindus; to name the religions which are best known in the West.

Ordinary people did not encounter these gods in their daily life: all that they knew about them was their manifestations in such phenomena as are mentioned above; and what they were told about them.

It seems likely that some enterprising people recognised in this concept a means for exercising power over the main bulk of the community. They purported to understand the gods; to have some form of contact with the gods; and to know the requirements of the gods. What resulted was a priesthood: a group who set themselves apart from the ordinary people and who demanded certain conduct from those ordinary people.

We have very little to tell us about the organisation of primitive tribes of millennia ago. We can try to draw inferences from archaeological material, such as ancient temples and images, the existence of which tell us that gods were worshipped. Sometimes we have records in writing from which we are able to infer the existence of a priesthood and the power which it wielded.

It is difficult, if not impossible, to escape the inference that the ordinary people were taught from an early age that the gods, whom the priests represented, were not figments of imagination, not theoretical or hypothetical concepts dreamed up as a possible explanation for the world in which they lived but, on the contrary, real beings of great power who must be obeyed.

Not only was it necessary to obey them, but it was also necessary to treat them with proper respect; to bow down before their images when so instructed by the priests; to provide sacrifices for them, even at great cost; to obey such detailed laws as the priests might state to be the requirements of the gods.

This power which the priesthood wielded, was also an important part of political power. Control of the tribe or state was not confined to royalty, or its equivalent such as the warrior chief. Neither of them was free to act without the approval, in some form or other, of the priesthood.

Even as recently as Elizabethan times, the kings of the Roman Catholic countries of Europe, e.g. Philip of Spain, would take their cue from the Vatican when considering foreign policy. It seems that it was the Pope who told Philip to send the Armada against England. The concept of the separation of matters

3

political from matters theological – the separation of the secular from the religious – is of very recent origin and very far from being universally accepted, even today. For example, it is not accepted by Islamic Fundamentalists; and there is reason to think that such a concept is in conflict with some of the basic ideas of Islam generally.

Some thousands of years ago the Jews introduced the concept of monotheism; that is to say that there is only one God who is responsible for everything. Some people think that this was a great step forwards for mankind. But why should they think that? It is true that it avoids the sort of quarrelling for which the stories of the Greek gods are famous; and it has led to the monotheism of Christians and Muslims. Yet it is not the view taken by Hindus, to whom there exist more that one god.

The monotheistic God is dignified by the use of a capital letter because those who take that view are entirely persuaded that such a being exists and has always existed.

Over the years, there grew up the mental discipline called 'theology'; the word which is defined in the Introduction.

There are arguments for saying that theology is really a branch of anthropology. That is defined as:-

'The science of the nature of man, embracing Human Physiology and Psychology'

Does anyone really *know* anything about God? (Note the emphasis). There is plenty of belief. To many, a belief so deep that it rules their lives. They become priests, nuns, monks; they perform all manner of dangerous and financially unrewarding tasks because they believe that their god has called them to do so. Some even kill themselves, as suicide bombers, because they believe that that is the wish of their god. So one cannot dismiss the power of this belief, but perhaps one can leaven it with some modern knowledge.

What is of immediate importance is to note that theology does not possess any means of testing the many hypotheses to which its debates and discussions give rise. It is essentially confined to a discussion on the same basis as that on which philosophers discuss philosophy; that is to say, a discussion of the interactions of the various topics which fall for consideration. In the case of theology, it is a discussion of the attributes of various gods, of the beliefs which are held about them, of the practices which those religions require; and, not least, of the meaning of the sacred texts on which those beliefs are founded.

It is the fact that every religion has at its base a set of written texts: sometimes referred to as Holy Scriptures. Many of those scriptures are old, e.g. those of the Jews and the Hindus. Some are of more recent origin, e.g. those of Christianity and Islam. In each case, those scriptures are accepted by believers as authoritative; that they derive their authority from God and must be accepted as embodying the authority of God. Many adherents consider them to be so authoritative that exegesis is forbidden.

* * * * * *

Over the years of the second millennium A.D. there has developed a wholly new way of thinking about the world in which we live. It was during the eighteenth century that it really began to flower and to turn into a mental discipline like none that preceded it. It acquired the name of 'science'.

That word has caused a lot of confusion.

First, it is best to put aside the word 'science' and to examine instead what is really involved, namely, the scientific method of thinking.

The scientific method of thought and analysis has proved to be a very powerful tool in the understanding of the Universe. The fact that it has primarily been applied to a study of the physical aspects of the world (as opposed to any 'spiritual' or moral aspects) has led many people to the view that such a method of reasoning can only produce that thing called 'science'; that it is separate from, and has no bearing upon, belief or 'faith'; that it can give no guide to morals or ethics; and that it really has nothing to do with, and is foreign to, mankind's ordinary existence.

Let us consider what science is really about.

First, it is to be noted that the root from which the word 'science' comes is a Latin one which means, quite simply,

5

'knowledge'. Although the Latin word is at least two thousand years old, the English usage is much more recent. There were some thinkers among the Ancient Greeks who studied the world and its workings, e.g. Archimedes; and Ptolemy. The former is most famous for his cry of 'Eureka', when he perceived the means of finding out whether a crown contained the amount of gold which it was supposed to contain. The latter in the second century A.D., having assumed that the Earth was at the centre of the Universe, proposed a complex set of rules for describing the paths through the heavens of the Sun and the planets; some of those rules even required some of the planets to go backwards at times. Then there was Aristotle who proposed that everything was made of earth, air, fire and water. And Eratosthenes who perceived that the world is round and made a remarkably accurate assessment of its diameter. It seems, however, that they regarded themselves, and were regarded, as philosophers.

Philosophy and science have much in common, e.g. in the mental processes of analysis and synthesis. The major difference lies in the desire of, and the attempts of, the scientist to find a way to test his hypotheses against the phenomena of the external world. The pure philosopher does not experiment; his hypotheses are evaluated only by logical debate.

The essence of the scientific method of reasoning lies in the deliberate acceptance of the existence of doubt. Thus, scientific reasoning is antithetical to any concept of Authority as a source of truth or understanding: all things are open to doubt, and every assertion must, so far as possible, be tested.

Karl Popper has argued that scientific theories can never be verified, only falsified. This is, in absolute terms, correct, in that it can be argued that it would take an infinity of successful tests to prove something conclusively. However, in the practical world in which we live, we can and do take as provisionally proven something which has been much tested and not yet found to be wrong.

What really happens, in respect of any experience which we have, and of which we 'feel' certain, is that the probabilities of the matter are so close to unity that we can and do ignore the small possibility that things might turn out differently next time we seek to test them.

Thus the approach of the scientific method is to test a hypothesis, in any way in which testing can be postulated, and to see whether the hypothesis is falsified by any of the tests.

In broad terms, the methodology which is accepted is to say that the higher the number of tests, and the more rigorous they are, which are successfully passed, the higher is the probability that the hypothesis is correct.

In pursuing this course, one frequently finds that a hypothesis is not completely falsified but that it applies only under limited circumstances; or is only 'correct so far as it goes'. This is the reality of what happened when Einstein showed, through the concept of relativity, that Newton's laws of gravity did not take account of a situation in which the bodies, whose gravitational relationship was under consideration, were moving rapidly in relation to each other.

Nevertheless, Newton's laws give us, for example, a sufficiently accurate picture of the motion of the Sun and Moon relative to the Earth to enable us to predict tides and eclipses without having to take relativity into account. That is so because the speed of the movement of the Moon relative to the Earth, and both of them relative to the Sun, is very low compared to the speed of light.

Lewis Wolpert has written a book called *The Unnatural Nature of Science*. He does not suggest that science deals only with things which are not natural. His point is that the facts about the Universe which scientists discover often seem to be contrary to our expectations and to our everyday experiences. Some of them seem so odd that scientists have themselves puzzled over the significance of their findings. It has been quipped that 'anyone who says he understands quantum mechanics, does not understand quantum mechanics'

It is commonly (but not universally) accepted that mankind has evolved from whatever his forebears were, and developed his ability to survive, both against the competition of the rest of the animal kingdom and in the face of the hostility of his environment.

He has survived without any clear understanding of how he was achieving it. His learning was entirely pragmatic. He learned that, if he got cut, blood came out; and he knew that he had a heart beating in his chest: but he had no idea that the heart was pumping the blood around his body. He knew that the Sun went down below the horizon in the evening and came up again the opposite side of the world the next morning: but he did not know that it was the Sun which was stationary, and that the world on which he stood was rotating. His 'common-sense' developed in order to enable him to survive, and it was quite unnecessary to that survival that he should understand such matters: he only needed practical knowledge, such as how to staunch a flow of blood; or that he should sleep during the dark to be ready for the next day.

It is worth pausing a moment to admire the extent to which he did learn to live with the environment in which he found himself. Think of the achievements of the Bushmen of South Africa; the Tuaregs of the Sahara; the Inuit of Greenland and North Canada; the Incas, the Aztec and the Maya of South America and their buildings. They were all remarkable and they achieved what they did without any basic understanding of how it was that what they did was so successful.

What he has learned through the application of the scientific method is frequently a matter of surprise when compared with the happy-go-lucky way he had developed his techniques for day-to-day survival. The point simply was that he knew what to do but had no way of knowing why it was the right thing to do: somebody, at some time, had tried it; it worked, and so everybody adopted it.

This is true even in comparatively modern fields of technology. In the Middle Ages, armourers learned how to make steel of various kinds: one sort hard and able to take an edge for swords; and another sort softer and able to yield, so as to be suitable for armour. They had learned, by trial and error what was the right thing to do to get these results. But they had no idea why it was the right thing to do. The modern science of metallurgy does know why.

The SOED contains a number of alternative meanings for the word 'science', none of which excludes particular areas of learning or knowledge; and one of which specifically includes the theological concept. A great deal of study, of a truly scientific kind, has been devoted to the texts and manuscripts on which the various religions of the world have been founded. Many areas of conflict have been found between the contents of the religious texts and historical facts as supported by secular records; and between different versions of what appear to be the same subject matter.

Are there, any aspects of mankind's relationship with the world which lie outside the proper purview of the scientific method of approach?

The application of the scientific method has already taught us much about how the world around us works; it is teaching us more and more about the manner in which we human beings work and why we act as we do. It will, in time, teach us more and more about why we have developed the ethics, the morals, and the cultures which we have. Why should it not enable us to reason out what would be the best and most successful ethics, morals and cultural patterns to enable us all to live in peace and side by side on this already overcrowded Earth? That is to say, to do so on a basis of agreement; and without regard to any supposed authoritative view, derived from belief in a supernatural entity, or in the absolute truth of the contents of an ancient religious text, as to what morals, ethics and cultural requirements we ought to have.

There exists one very important consequence of applying the scientific approach. When a proposition has been well tested and accepted, it is accepted by all who have studied the evidence.

From that point on, there does not exist among them an alternative view; unless and until it is displaced by another, and better-supported proposition. For example, Maxwell's laws of electro-magnetism, developed in the nineteenth century, are accepted world wide as correctly describing how electricity and magnetism are related. The above reference to Einstein and Newton is an example of a partial replacement of an older proposition by a newer one.

In contrast, no universal truth exists in religion. Not only is there diversity between the many different religions but, even inside a single religion, one finds differences of view; e.g. as between Catholic and Protestant; or between Sunni and Shiite Muslims. Or even more acute, the difference of view within the Anglican Christians as to the status to be accorded to homosexuals; and whether women can be made priest or bishops.

The various religions cannot even agree as to whether there is only one God or several. And this is the position in the 21st century despite many centuries of the existence of those religions and of discussion about and between them; and despite the immediacy of worldwide communications, and the speed of modern travel.

This ought to tell us that none of them has yet got to the bottom of the matter; that is to say, to a correct understanding of the real nature of God and his relationship with the Universe and mankind. Regrettably, it seems that the adherents of each religion believe that theirs holds the correct view. Can they all be right? And if not, how is the human race to get to the bottom of this problem and find out the universal truth about God?

Even more seriously, how are we all to live together if one lot of us has one set of laws and morals and another lot has a different set? Those who have had to concern themselves with such matters as the relationship between immigrant Muslims and local inhabitants who are not Muslim, know that this is a real problem.

It is the proper business of scientists to keep on probing everything which they can so as to learn as much as can be known; including as much as can be learned about our own nature and about how and why mankind holds the various beliefs about God, and gods, which he does.

This also should be remembered: When scientists have discovered and verified a fact, it is a fact of the Universe. It is a fact of Jehovah, of Jesus, of the Christian God, of Allah, of Krishna, of Ganesh; and of any other gods you care to name. If somebody says that such a fact is in conflict with a religious truth, let him beware. Should he continue to believe that the religious truth is correct; or should he accept that that fact must prevail? The history of the acceptance of what Charles Darwin said is very much to the point here.

2

Programming

That word is a noun constructed from the verb – to program. There was no such verb listed in the 1967 edition of the SOED. There was a noun, defined so as to be understood in the sense of a theatre or concert program.

Since 1967, the verb has come into common use in the field of computers. It refers to the act or acts by which a computer is given instructions to enable it to carry out some operation when fed with an appropriate factual input.

The typescript of this book was typed on a Sony VAIO computer which, when purchased, was already loaded with Microsoft Windows XP. The latter is a program which enables one, by performing various operations on the computer keyboard, to type in letters so that they are displayed on a screen; and to correct mistakes and do many other things. Since then other programs have been added to the computer, e.g. one which enables a printer to receive instructions from the computer to cause it to print text which has been typed with the aid of Windows.

The distinction between those two programs is important to what follows. Windows was in the machine from the outset. The printer program was added later. These two aspects of programming have particular interest in relation to the way in which living things grow and behave and learn.

In 1953 Watson and Crick elucidated the structure of DNA, the material by which genetic instructions are handed on from one generation to the next. Since then a great deal has been learned about DNA and what it does. That knowledge enables us to appreciate much more about living things than was previously possible. It may, nevertheless, be observed in passing that there remains a very great deal more to learn.

11

DNA works by means of a code of surprising simplicity. DNA is made up of four different chemical units, designated A, C, G and T. These, combined in threes, provide a code in which each triplet denotes one of a number of amino acids which are the chemical building blocks from which proteins are made. This code is 'read' by things in the cell, be it plant or animal, whereby the cell is instructed what to make.

Thus, a wheat seed contains the DNA which causes the germ of the seed to grow into a wheat plant. Similarly, that tiny speck in, say, a robin's egg, also often called the germ, contains the program of instructions for making the robin. But it also contains instructions for very much more besides. A robin does not have to be taught to mate with a robin of the opposite sex, rather than with a tit or a finch. Its DNA contained the necessary instructions to get that right. Similarly, with the instructions how to sing a robin's song and how to build a robin's nest. Furthermore, that DNA contains the orders which compel the robin to incubate its eggs, and to feed its fledglings until they can look after themselves.

Other animals are similarly instructed by their DNA: Thus a foal can stand and run within about half an hour of being born; and it knows where its mother's teats are and how to suck them.

It is worth noting that, in general, all this behaviour is carried on from generation to generation without the young receiving instruction from its parents: it is all in the DNA. There are some creatures where the parents teach the young, e.g. the teaching of hunting skills by a lioness, but this is not the rule.

The DNA, under the guidance of which a human baby grows, does not contain instructions enabling it to stand so soon, nor even to find its mother's teats, but it does contain instructions on how to suck when a teat is put in its mouth and on how to make a noise which will attract its mother's attention. Similarly, a spider hatches from the egg with the knowledge of how to make a web.

The point is that most living creatures, if not all of them, carry in their DNA not only directions as to how the creature is to be constructed, but also how it is to behave, at least in the early days of its life.

Such inherited programming can be quite complicated. For example, members of the cat tribes, once they have opened their eyes and found the ability to stand and run, will play. This play is not just for amusement, if for that at all; in fact, it serves the cat as a training course for the more serious business of hunting and catching prey when it has to fend for itself.

The second kind of programming is also found in animals; that is the capacity to learn to do something for which it is not inherently programmed. Thus, there are animals which can be taught to do things which it is not normal for them to do as a result of their genetic programming. For example, a parrot can be taught to speak and a chimpanzee to wear clothes and drink tea at a tea party. Indeed, there are many animals which can be thus programmed and are so programmed as a matter of course in everyday life, from the horse to the guide dog for the blind. This latter kind of programming is different from the first in a vital respect: it involves alteration to the brain; that is to say, whatever was the organisation of the brain before that programming, it is different after. It is somewhat similar to loading a printer program into the computer as referred to above.

We have also learned that, sometimes, there are defects in the genetic programming. For example, it is now known that some diseases, e.g. spina bifida and Huntington's chorea, result from errors in the DNA, that is to say, from pieces of DNA which are not in the normal pattern for a normal human being. Now that this has been recognised, much work is being done in trying to find ways to combat the defect. What is obvious, but needs saying for reasons which will appear hereafter, is that the person afflicted with such a defect cannot, by himself, still less merely by thinking about it, do anything to put it right: he needs all the help which modern medical knowledge can give.

The second kind of programming applies with even greater force to humans than it does to other animals. So far as present knowledge goes, there seems to be no limit to the amount we are capable of learning. Unfortunately, there are some aspects of this programming which we, as individuals, have great

13

difficulty in recognising as programming, and which we, therefore, have great difficulty in reviewing in the light of any new knowledge which is presented to us.

It is the fact, although it is seldom recognised to be such, that the accumulated programming to which an individual is subjected during early years is what we call 'culture'. I know a family in which one parent is English and one French. Three children were born and, in their early years brought up, in England: they are recognisably English. A fourth child was born and brought up, including going to school, in France. That child has the mannerisms of a French person and speaks English with a French accent. Yet, for all of them, their genetic make-up came from the same two parents. Their differences are cultural and arise from the different cultural programming to which they were subjected during their formative years.

Experience teaches us that this cultural programming is difficult to alter once a child has reached a certain age. There is no fundamental reason why an individual should be unable to recognise it for what it is. However, experience teaches that the vast majority of people are quite unable to accept that some of what they take for granted, or believe to be immutable truths, may be no more than part of the programming which they received as a child.

Nowhere is this more true than in the field of religion. A child adopts the religion of its parents because it has been brought up, i.e. programmed, to believe both that that religion is truth which must be accepted and is the only true religion. Some change their religion. Some cease to be believers in religion. But these are the unusual ones. Most go on believing, all their lives, that the religion in which they were brought up contains the only acceptable rules for life. They go to church on Sundays; or they go to prayers in the mosque on Fridays; or they regard divorce as impossible; and so on. It seems to be impossible for most of them to examine their beliefs in the light of facts and arguments put before them and to change their beliefs.

If you are interested to see the extent to which cultural programming can induce a barbaric state of mind, even at the end of the 20th century, read the book *Infidel* by Ayaan Hirsi Ali. In it she tells of the experiences which she had to endure as a girl brought up in a Muslim environment in a Somali family.

It is a reasonable inference that no new knowledge had penetrated that culture in the centuries since Mohammed. She is obviously intelligent and she has an open and enquiring mind. She asked questions which nobody answered. It took her a very long time to realise the falsity of much of what she had been told and taught; and that it has no basis in fact or reason. Her experience exemplifies the way in which such programming blinds one to the possibility of doubting what one has been taught; and the very real difficulty faced by any such person in trying to get an unbiased answer to questions.

This book also illustrates the extremely rigid and primitive attitude to the world which is portrayed by Islam in the absence of exegesis in the light of modern knowledge. Regrettably, the vast bulk of the human race seems to be unable to recognise which parts of their beliefs and personality are the result of programming, and might advantageously be re-examined and perhaps revised, in the light of what we have learned about this Universe, and ourselves within it, in the last few hundred years.

When I say 'advantageously', I have in mind benefit to the community as a whole; in particular benefit to those among whom they live but who have been programmed into a different culture and beliefs.

Here I wish to pose some questions, the mere asking of which is likely to result in me being accused of racism or lack of political correctness. I am not a racist. I am concerned with cultural differences; not with differences of human physical characteristics.

In some parts of the world where Islam is the predominant religion, it is the practice of the Muezzin to go to the top of the minaret and call the faithful to prayer. This practice originated in the 7th Century when clocks were not the universal thing which they are today and when it was necessary to alert the public to the fact that the time had arrived to pray or to go to the mosque. With the aid of modern technology it is not unknown for him to speak from the ground and use loudspeakers to amplify his voice. Is it possible that, in other countries, such conduct might disturb the neighbourhood? If it does upset people who are not of Islam, is that not a reason for discontinuing that practice? Can that practice be abandoned without peril to the souls of those of Islam? Would it be advantageous to the community at large to reach some kind of accommodation between those of Islam and the rest?

Questions such as these arise in all walks of life and, if those concerned were able to recognise that which is programming and can be changed, and distinguish it from other aspects of programming, such as respect for truth, there might be a lot less friction among human beings.

To revert to the first kind of programming, i.e. the genetic one, it has recently been postulated that certain types of anti-social conduct, for example a propensity to steal, may be caused by, or precipitated by, or aggravated by, something in the person's DNA.

Hitherto, the concept of sin and the doctrine of free will have led to a view that each of us is wholly responsible for our conduct. We recognise that upbringing can affect a person's behaviour but the general view has been that the individual has a personal responsibility and that an antisocial person must, if possible, be re-educated into a less anti-social way of life. However, what we may have to face up to in the future is the possibility that some people have a genetic propensity to anti- social behaviour and are no more able to put that right by taking thought than can a victim of spina bifida or Huntington's chorea cure himself by thinking about it.

Unfortunately, there are some people who find such a concept impossible to assimilate; who condemn it because it conflicts with their preconceived ideas about morality; and who will not allow of the possibility that medical attention, rather than prison, may prove to be the way forward. More fortunately, there are people who consider the possibility too important to neglect, and who are doing research into it. This is not really a completely new idea. We have now become accustomed to the idea that there are people, such as psychopaths, who have an inborn propensity for violence, and even for murder. Such murderers are not regarded as deliberately breaking a law of which they were aware; but as being unable by reason of their mental defect, to appreciate that they ought not to act as they do.

This last point is a part of the old debate of 'Nature versus Nurture'. It comes up from time to time in various forms: often in the context of a comparison of the abilities of members of different races. Many times the question has been raised whether those of African descent have, by nature, less intelligence than those with white skins. The arguments are usually based on so-called intelligence tests. But those tests are devised and performed without paying any regard to the cultural differences between the races and the relevance of the tests to those of a different culture. The question has also been raised in reference to differences which appear to exist in some aspects of the sporting world, e.g. boxing and sprinting.

No attempt whatever will be made here to debate such matters. The point which is made, however, is that there is not the slightest justification for attempting to stifle that debate. There are many who shout 'racist' whenever such questions are raised. They are foolish to do so because, by doing so, they may stifle enquiry which could benefit us all. For example, if rigorous acceptable tests showed that black sprinters do sprint better than white ones, enquiry might assist the white ones to improve their performance. And it might emerge from such enquiry that a properly constituted intelligence test would show that blacks are as intelligent as, or perhaps more intelligent than, whites. In all such cases, to ask the question, and to find out the reason for differences, or apparent differences, can only be of value to us all. It would advance our knowledge of the world in which we live and that can never be a disadvantage.

Consider an example which nobody could regard as racist. There are (or certainly were) some people in Africa who were small because they were undernourished or did not have a properly balanced diet. There are others who are small because that is what their genetic makeup dictates. An adequate and proper diet can increase the stature of the former but it will make no difference to the latter. The enquiry which led to the realisation that there was malnutrition did good, not harm.

17

It is regrettable that there are some who consider that too much knowledge can be dangerous. They are wrong. It is not the knowledge that is dangerous, but what one does with it. Indeed, an important area in which the extension of knowledge would be of advantage to the vast bulk of humanity would be to find out why some people wish to use knowledge to the disadvantage of others.

That is a question on which moralists and priests have expressed many views over the centuries, and on which psychologists are struggling to make some headway.

There is another area of activity which gives rise to conflict: that is the use of schools to indoctrinate children into a religion. Historically, a number of the early charitable schools in the UK were founded and run by various Christian denominations. This gave an opportunity, of which the maximum use was made, to indoctrinate the pupils into the particular denomination of the school's founders; in other words, to program them. There seems to be a general desire among religious believers to try and persuade others to adopt their views. When education was made a state obligation in the 19th century, many of those schools were allowed to continue their indoctrination while receiving state financial support. As a result we have, for example, Church of England schools.

The founding fathers of the USA took a different line. They made it illegal for a state school to conduct any kind of religious ceremony: not even morning prayers of a non-denominational kind. This division between state and church has persisted and it is left to the parents to indoctrinate a child into a religion, or not to indoctrinate at all. Interestingly, there is evidence to suggest that, despite this division (or perhaps because of it?), church-going and religious belief are stronger in USA than in UK. So far as the UK is concerned, there is still conflict between those who wish to have religious indoctrination permitted in state-funded schools and those who do not.

For example, Muslims have been asking for state funding to enable them to run schools in which the pupils are indoctrinated into the principles and practices of the Muslim religion. This, if done, would be a regrettable step: it would be far better to adopt the American practice and withdraw state support from all schools which undertake such indoctrination. This would help to move our society towards one in which religious matters and secular ones are separated: a society which would more readily address its political problems on a basis of what is good for all, regardless of religious and cultural differences, even if it thereby became impossible to provide a political basis which satisfied people of all religions and cultures. Those who were not satisfied would have to accept that what was done was done 'for the greatest good of the greatest number'; as, indeed, they have to do in respect of all political decisions in a democratic society.

Is there any doubt that the USA has the right idea and that all state-funded schools should be entirely secular. That is not to say that the children are not to be educated as to the nature and beliefs of all other religions; but that is very different from indoctrinating them. To inform is very different from programming.

3

The Watershed of
Charles Darwin

Charles Darwin is famous for having perceived, and taught in his book called *The Origin of Species*, published in 1859, the concept of Evolution by Natural Selection. The emergence of this concept has been a true watershed in the history of human thought about the living world; including ourselves. It has had its impact, not only on the world of science, but also on the world of theology.

There is a popular misconception about what he taught which it is important to dispel. He did not teach that changes are brought about by the competition between species. For example, he did not teach that giraffes have long necks today because their forebears continually stretched up for leaves on trees and thereby stretched their necks and then passed that on to their offspring. Even though he was, of course, unaware of DNA, Darwin appreciated that a change from a parent to its offspring occurs randomly. The genetic make-up of an individual is set at a very early point in its life cycle. The eggs in the ovary of a human female are formed at the foetal stage: they are only altered thereafter by an external influence such as nuclear radiation, chemical action, or mistranscription of DNA.

It was Lamarck who had proposed in 1809 that characteristics acquired by a creature during its life could be passed on to its offspring: that view is now totally discredited. It was the view propounded by Lysenko in Stalin's time. Stalin accepted what Lysenko said and accepted his assertion that wheat would evolve to be able to grow in cold climates, if it was exposed to such climates. Stalin gave orders for this advice to adopted. It was bad advice and, as a result, many thousands died of starvation.

What Darwin taught was that the changes which occur between a parent and its offspring are themselves random events over which the individual has no control. As a result of such a change, the offspring differs in some respect from its parent. It is only after that difference has emerged that Natural Selection has a part to play. If the effect of the difference is to give the offspring some advantage over creatures which are (or quite generally an environment which is) in competition with it, that individual may survive to pass on the difference to its offspring; and so on down the generations, so that the difference may become established and may even supplant that from which it sprang.

What matters is whether the trait in question not only confers some advantage, but also whether it operates in such a way that the trait can be passed on. Thus, whatever the trait does to the individual, it must not preclude the individual from reproducing.

A particularly striking, and to us, gruesome, example can be found in the practice of a female praying mantis eating its mate and of the mate submitting rather than attempting to escape (as some spiders do). The male is not eaten until after copulation; by then the genes of the male have been passed to the eggs of the female. The female gets the benefit of extra protein by eating its mate. In the result, the male, by allowing himself to be eaten, has improved the chances of his own genes being propagated. His submission therefore has survival value in the competitive world of Natural Selection. If it did not have that value, one could be fairly certain that the trait would not have survived.

It can be seen that, underlying what Darwin taught, is the concept of a world which advances, not by an orderly and pre-ordained series of steps, but by a series of 'experiments'; that is to say by the trial, by an offspring, of a mutation. The outcome of that trial depends upon the interaction of all the factors of the environment in which each 'experiment' is performed. It is over many millions of years, and as the end result of virtually as many such experiments, that the Earth on which we live, and its flora and fauna, and us, have arrived at the form which we see about us today.

In addition, we know today that many more factors were at play than were appreciated in Darwin's time. For example, we know that the continents rest upon vast tectonic plates which are always on the move. The Atlantic Ocean is getting wider by about 15 cm each year. Australia was joined to South America many millions of years ago, at a time when there were no placental mammals, or very few: most, if not all, mammals were marsupial. It seems that there were no placental mammals on the land mass which became Australia after separation from South America. As a result, the marsupials survived in Australia because they did not have to deal with competition from placentals. The superiority of the latter has resulted in the effective elimination of marsupials from the rest of the world. The opossums, and related species, in the Americas are the only ones which have managed to survive.

Since the discovery of DNA, its helical structure, and the manner in which it replicates itself, a great deal of knowledge has been added to Darwin's basic thesis. It is now apparent that each living thing is born as it is or, if a vegetable, grows from the seed as it does, because its DNA makes it do so. That DNA cannot be altered by anything done by the living thing itself: the only changes possible are mutations, which are not under the control of the thing itself. Thus, it is the stepwise changes in DNA, due to mutations, which bring about the diversity which led Darwin to his conclusions.

Some people have argued that this cannot be correct because, they say, such a complex thing as an eye cannot have arisen by a stepwise series of changes. Such a pronouncement must be stigmatised as based on ignorance. It may be as difficult for such a person to perceive the steps by which such a development could occur, as it would be for anyone unacquainted with them to understand how a computer or a television set works. Such is the enormous spread of our knowledge today, that it is necessary for anyone of us who wishes to debate about such matters to prepare himself by a great deal of study first.

Those who have so prepared themselves entertain no doubt that the stepwise system of changes can produce as complicated a thing as an eye. This same process is responsible for the existence of those creatures whose habits seem, to most of us and to put it mildly, to be unpleasant; such as the praying mantis and those wasps which deposit their eggs in a caterpillar so that, when it hatches, the wasp larva eats the living caterpillar from inside.

In short, if life is to be possible in a universe which is constructed as ours is, it is just as possible for the things which we stigmatise as unpleasant to evolve as it is for those we find pleasant. Thus we have bacteria, viruses, parasites and much else besides. Whether any particular life form does so evolve or, if it evolves, survive, depends upon all the surrounding circumstances: what the outcome will be is a matter of statistical probability. If it exists today, the probabilities favoured it: if they did not, it is extinct.

Darwin's concept was a watershed in its theological impact. Until then, the Christian world accepted the Biblical concept of creation by God in which God deliberately created the world as it is and deliberately created mankind as a separate exercise. What Darwin said raised doubts about that; and has led to much disputation which is still going on today.

In about 1650 Bishop Usher had calculated the age of the Earth from the contents of the Bible and concluded that it was created in 4004 B.C. There was an obvious conflict between Darwin and Usher: if Usher was right, there was not enough time for what Darwin proposed to have happened. However, by the time of Darwin's work, the discoveries of geologist had made it seem unlikely that Usher's calculation gave the correct answer. In fact, it was not until the 20th century, after the discovery of radioactivity, that a really satisfactory estimate of the age of the Earth became available; that is to say, an estimate which plausibly accounted for what was known about ancient fossils, about the age of rocks and mountains, about the movement of tectonic plates, and about the decay of radioactive minerals. In round figures, the Earth is now estimated to be about 4 thousand million years old: a length of time which is considered sufficient to provide scope for Darwin's thesis.

In the famous debate on Darwin's theory at Oxford in June 1860 Bishop Wilberforce ridiculed Darwin's suggestion that mankind was not created by God as a unique act as described in the Book of Genesis, but was descended over many generations from ape-like creatures. Replying to the bishop, T.H. Huxley aptly said that man has no reason to be ashamed of having an ape for his grandfather. He would feel more shame if his ancestor were a man of ignorance and blind religious prejudice.

Even in more recent times, theologians have had difficulty in accepting that his thesis was one of reality rather than just another theory. Thus, as recently as 1950, Pope Pius XII, in *Humani Generis*, expressed the view that Darwin's concept was not proven, but was still to be regarded as a theory which, being in conflict with Catholic doctrine, might yet be disproved. He was, by so asserting, taking a similar line to that taken against Galileo. He was setting a belief in theological dogma, and a belief in the inerrancy of Holy Scripture, against knowledge obtained by application of the scientific method. As in the case of Galileo, retreat became necessary.

That retreat took place in October 1996 when Pope John Paul publicly acknowledged that Darwin's thesis could no longer be regarded as mere theory: it was supported so substantially that even the Roman Catholic Church had to accept that mankind was 'descended from monkeys' rather than being a separate and distinct creation of God. He asserted that there was no conflict between accepting that and the Catholic doctrine that God placed a soul in each human body.

This idea of God placing a soul in each body has led to discussion about when God places it there. This is a discussion which is relevant to other aspects of Catholic doctrine.

First is the assertion that abortion is wrong because, inter alia, it destroys a body in which God has implanted a soul. This assertion, in turn, raises the question: when does God implant the soul? Here the position which the Vatican adopted was to say that it happened at the moment of conception. One can see that, to have said otherwise, would have left open a window of time in which abortion could take place without interfering with a soul.

What does not seem to have been taken into account is that 30% or more of conceptions are spontaneously aborted. This form of abortion is often called miscarriage. It is unnecessary to delve into the question why this spontaneous abortion should occur, nor into the question of what happens to the foetuses so aborted. However, that matter of spontaneous abortion is a fact and it would seem to raise this question: if God puts a soul into the foetus at conception, what happens to all those souls of aborted foetuses? A whole raft of theological questions flow from that one; e.g. will they go to hell because the foetuses which contained them died unshriven? Or because they were not interred with proper ceremony?

But that is not all. In recent years there has been developed, and now much used, a technique for helping couples who wish to have a child, but who fail to achieve conception by normal copulation. It is called In Vitro Fertilization. In its simplest form, one or more eggs are removed from the woman's ovary and injected with the nucleus of a sperm from the man. The resulting embryo is allowed to multiply to a few cells and then, if all has gone well, implanted in the woman's uterus. It is common to use more than one egg as a safeguard against failure: sometimes to implant more than one; sometimes to destroy the unwanted ones.

The interesting question is: when did God implant a soul?

One way out of this problem is to change the date at which God is considered to place a soul in a body. We are dealing here with a problem on which Holy Scripture gives no guidance because the possibility of such a problem could not be envisaged those many centuries ago. If one looks at that problem in the light of modern knowledge, one is faced with the difficulty of identifying the moment between conception and birth at which it can be said that God performed that act. A possible moment is that of implantation; if implantation does not take place an embryo cannot grow. However that only eliminates a small proportion of the spontaneous abortions: the great majority of them happen after implantation.

There is another problem, which may be more fundamental, flowing from the assertion by Christians that God places a soul in each human body. If one studies Darwin's thesis, especially as elaborated in the light of fossil finds made since his time, and in the light of comparisons of our DNA with that of various apes and monkeys, one learns that it teaches that there was an Ancestral Creature from which at least 3 lines have evolved: the gorillas, the chimpanzees, and us. But we evolved through a chain of intermediates many of whose fossils have been found and dated, including various hominids, homo erectus, and homo sapiens, which is us.

The first question is to ask when, speaking in historical terms, did God first implant a soul in a body? Did that not happen until a distinct homo sapiens had emerged? Or did it happen to homo erectus? Or even earlier to one of the hominids? What distinction was there between each stage of that evolution? Or was there a soul in that Ancestral Creature; and in Neanderthal man? Is there one in a chimpanzee and a gorilla?

These are not idle questions, but indications of serious conflict between knowledge and belief. And if it is right, as asserted earlier, that these known facts are as binding on God as on us, what are we to suppose is the real truth about God's implantation of souls?

The acknowledgement of the soundness of Darwin's thesis also has a bearing on the notion that mankind was initially free of sin and then suffered a Fall: a topic which is covered in Genesis and on which John Milton wrote at length in *Paradise Lost*. That notion does not seem easily compatible with the idea of a development through a series of species. Was homo erectus capable of sin or Neanderthal man? And, even more worrying: what is the nature of sin? This is discussed in another chapter but it may be noted here that it is difficult to reconcile the notion of sin with an absence of moral awareness.

Let me suggest another explanation of that aspect of human behaviour which has led to some conduct being stigmatised as sinful: that is that the creatures of the more primitive stages of that evolution were as animal as the Ancestral Creature (or as any undomesticated animal) and only learned how to be 'good' as a result of being able to talk and of living in communities. When that happened, mankind had to develop behavioural traits which would make it possible for people to live together. Over the generations he developed those characteristics which make that possible and which have given him the complex cultures which he has today. If that is right, sin is no more than a breach of the rules of that culture; and is not a matter involving failure to comply with the divine.

Problems like this did not arise until those who believed their propositions of religious dogma found themselves forced to retreat, step by step, from positions previously taken up. When will they recognise this dilemma? How will they deal with it? What new problems will eventuate one cannot tell. All that can be said with some certainty, judging from the past, is that the pressure of knowledge, based on scientific thought and discoveries, will continue to force changes in beliefs.

Much of the above discussion has been based on details of Roman Catholic theology because that is well-known to most of us and is readily verifiable. But other religions are equally exposed to the consequences of what Darwin has taught the world.

A general thought which emerges from what Darwin said, and which is reinforced by what we have learned from Quantum Mechanics, is that everything we know tells us that the happenings in this Universe are not regulated, as it were, by a composer's score, not even if allowance is made for a conductor to impose his own interpretation. There are basic rules which govern what happens but, beyond that, everything that happens, happens on what may be called an 'experimental' basis. That is, after all, the way in which Natural Selection works on mutated species: they are exposed to their environment and either survive or fail. It would not have been possible to predict in the far distant past that dinosaurs would evolve; nor that we would. Nor would it ever be possible to predict where and when mutations would occur. Darwin, in effect, dealt a serious blow to the theory that if, at a given time one knew everything about the state of the Universe, one could predict its future in detail.

Here is an interesting question arising out of Darwin's work and its ultimate acceptance, e.g. by the Vatican in 1996. Why is it that all theologians have not become agnostic about every question which scientists raise on the issue whether a phenomenon has, or will eventually be proved to have, a scientific explanation; as opposed to being explicable only by the concept of divine action? Time and again they disparage suggestions that something seemingly spiritual has a mundane explanation. See '*Credo*' by the Chief Rabbi in *The Times* newspaper of Saturday 6th October 2007.

There is another topic to which Darwin's principles are relevant, and that is the matter of homosexuality. It is a topic which has much exercised the Christian Churches over recent times, because of Biblical references which are said to condemn it as sinful. There has been, and still is, much debate about the nature of homosexuality. It is another example of the 'nature or nurture' argument. The question is often debated whether homosexuality results from the individual's genetic make-up or is a cultural phenomenon resulting from the exposure of the individual, at an impressionable age or time, to the experience of homosexual conduct. In the latter case, it would rightly be understood as an example of cultural programming.

The only consideration which is relevant here is the impact of Darwin's teaching on the question whether homosexuality is genetically driven.

Heterosexuality has evolved as the only way in which genetic variation can be spread from generation to generation. Asexual propagation results in each generation having the same genetic make-up as that of its forebears: except when there is an intervening mutation, in which case all succeeding generations from that individual, if they survive, have the mutation. Sexual propagation, whether in plants or animals, results in the mixing of the genes from the two parents. With very few exceptions, the genes of the male and female differ as a result of the diversity produced by evolution, and by sexual propagation over millions of years. Heterosexual intercourse has, as its prime function, that of producing the next generation. Whatever other values it may have acquired, in humans, it undoubtedly discharges that fundamental function.

Sexual relations, whatever their nature, between two individuals of the same sex, have, and can have, no effect on the genetic make-up of the next generation: because they do not produce a next generation. If homosexuality is a genetically based trait, it cannot be regarded as a mutation having a potential for improvement of the species by Natural Selection: because homosexual relationships cannot result in homosexual predilections being passed on to the next generation by a homosexual act.

For reasons which will shortly appear, I interpose here a few words about cystic fibrosis. It is a most unfortunate disease for those who are afflicted and frequently prevents them from living beyond the early twenties. Modern DNA research has established that it results from an error in transcription of a single base letter in a particular gene. It is only if both parents have the defect that the child will have it. If only one has it the other good half of the gene makes reasonable health possible; but that child can pass the defect on. Thus cystic fibrosis has persisted and will go on persisting but will manifest itself unexpectedly.

If the nature of homosexuality is as set out above, it is a genetic trait having a characteristic similar to those of cystic fibrosis and spina bifida. That is to say, it is a trait which is passed on to succeeding generations in a concealed form; a form which does not necessarily always manifest itself in those who have that genetic variant. Perhaps, like that of cystic fibrosis, such a variant only becomes active if both parents have it. If that is so, can it be regarded as anything other than an unfortunate aberration like cystic fibrosis, having regard to the fact that it confers no survival advantage?

It may be contrasted with the gene for sickle cell anaemia which, despite having the disadvantage that it causes a reduced ability to use oxygen in the blood, has the side-effect that it confers a measure of immunity to malaria. That is so because the malarial parasite cannot enter the sickle-shaped blood corpuscle. Instead of dying out because of the disadvantage, that variant has survived in those parts of the world where malaria is prevalent.

Thus a gene for homosexuality, if it exists, may be contrasted with the gene which confers altruistic behaviour on the male praying mantis, and thereby increases its reproductive potential.

If it is a culturally programmed trait, that makes an additional reason why it cannot be passed on to the next generation; and that is because the genetic information which is passed on to the next generation cannot be affected by anything done by the individual. Changes in the genetic make-up of an individual can only result from mutation.

Hence, if homosexuality is a cultural trait, i.e. one acquired as a result of post-natal programming, it does not differ from any other acquired trait, such as a predilection for alcohol or drugs.

Whether the above discussion is of assistance to troubled Christians, must be left for them to decide.

4

Quantum Mechanics

Quantum Mechanics can fairly be regarded as one of the most astonishing sets of rules which has ever emerged from mankind's efforts to understand the Universe in which he lives. Not only does it depart from all the ideas of classical physics but it is about as counter-intuitive as any set of ideas could be.

First, an explanation of how it arose.

As the nineteenth century was drawing to a close there was nothing to indicate the revolution in thought, in the world of physics, which the twentieth would bring. There were recognised to be a number of problems to which there was not even the beginning of an answer, e.g. what was the source of the enormous outpouring of energy from the sun. Furthermore, there was nothing in what was known which cast its shadow before to suggest the possibility of what has become known as Quantum Mechanics.

The concept grew out of a particular puzzle concerned with heat. You will know that as something heats up, e.g. a poker in a fire, its colour changes from a dull red towards white. In the case of the filament of an electric lamp, it is a brilliant white because it is very hot. Careful measurement had been made of the relationship between temperature and colour and the graph relating the two was well known. However, it had defeated the best brains to find an explanation for that relationship.

Max Planck was asked to have a look at this problem. There is a legend that he looked at it as a mathematician rather than as a physicist: that is to say, that he tried to find a mathematical formula which would fit the curve rather than try to think up a physical explanation for the phenomenon. He did find a formula which was a very good fit. He published it without it attracting a great deal of attention at the time. It had a quirk. It indicated that the colour did not change smoothly as the temperature increased but that it changed in small steps; remaining at a particular colour while the temperature rose a little and then changing suddenly to a new colour. These steps were so small as not to be perceptible to the eye. The name 'quantum' was given to such a step.

Put shortly, what this showed is that energy does not flow in a continuous stream: it flows in a succession of small packets. Now known as 'quanta'.

The further developments of this concept can be found set out in many books. It led to an understanding of atomic and nuclear structure, to an explanation of radioactivity and to many other things, including the source of the Sun's heat and the reason why lava from a volcano is red hot. It has been well said that Quantum Mechanics is perhaps the most fully tried and tested concept that has ever come out of scientific research. It is, for example, the basis on which transistors, microchips and computers are designed; and it has led to a greatly improved understanding of the Universe in which we live and, in particular, of many phenomena observed in astronomy.

Among the things to which it led is a group of three principles which have radically altered the view which should be taken of this Universe. They are:-

1. Pauli's exclusion principle.
2. Heisenberg's uncertainty principle.
3. The principle embodied in Schroedinger's wave equations.

It had long been thought that an atom comprised a nucleus and one or more electrons; but little was understood about their interrelationship. That interrelationship, as explained by Quantum Mechanics, is most easily understood by thinking of the electrons as moving in orbits around the nucleus rather as the different planets move in orbits around the sun. It is now also known that an electron in orbit around a nucleus has what is called 'spin'. That can conveniently be thought of as being like the rotation of the Earth on its own axis. However, an electron can have either of two states of spin.

Pauli's Exclusion Principle says that it is impossible for two electrons of a given atom to occupy the same orbit and have the same spin. The work of Neils Bohr and others led to the conclusion that, when a nucleus has more than one electron, they arrange themselves so that the orbits closest to the nucleus are filled preferentially. Indeed, even in the case of hydrogen, with its single electron, that electron will get as close as it can to the nucleus. If you add energy to an atom, e.g. by heating it, it causes the electrons to move outwardly away from the nucleus. The outermost electron will be the first to move to an orbit further away from the nucleus. The electrons do that as the atom absorbs the heat. Conversely, as the electrons fall back towards the nucleus, the atom radiates energy in the form of electromagnetic radiation; in other words as light or radiant heat.

Pauli's principle gives us an explanation of something which we all take for granted: that we live in a stable Universe. But for the effect of the phenomenon denoted by that principle, there would be nothing to stop electrons winding their way inwards towards the nucleus, radiating energy as they did so, and everything in the Universe would have become dead and cold long ago.

In everyday terms that stability manifests itself in what we take for granted in the world around us. The chair which you sat on before you went to bed will still be there in the morning. The wood of which it is made will not have turned into something else. And you yourself will still be you. Have you ever asked yourself why that should be so? We now know that the explanation lies in the fact that this Universe has been constructed to operate in accordance with the principles of Quantum Mechanics.

An important fact about the world which we know is that every substance which we encounter is of moderate density. In fact, the material of which an atomic nucleus is made is of extraordinarily high density. However, the electrons orbit at so great a distance from the nucleus, in relation to its size, that everyday matter is as we know it. If it were not for that distance, matter would have a density of many thousands of tons to the cubic inch. Such high density is, in fact, found in neutron stars; these are stars which have burned out in such a way that their electrons have gone and the nuclei have collapsed together under the influence of gravity. A star which is several times more massive than the Sun, will end as a neutron star; or, if it is really large, as a Black Hole. But it is this moderate density which makes possible all those phenomena which we know as chemistry and which, therefore, make life possible.

Now to Heisenberg's Uncertainty Principle: this states that it is impossible to know both the precise location of an atomic particle, e.g. an electron, and the precise speed and precise direction of its movement. The word 'precise' is the important one. There is always a measure of uncertainty. That measure is defined in terms of a quantity known as Planck's Constant.

What is involved here is not a matter of a limitation on a human being's ability to measure something. It is a matter of a fundamental property of the Universe, which is so constructed that it is impossible to know that such an electron possesses both a precise location and a precise direction and speed of movement. It is inherent in the nature of things that any attempt to make those measurements must impart energy to the electron; and so alter its position, or its velocity or the direction in which it moves. And this is true of every particle at the atomic scale of things, e.g. a proton or neutron or an atom itself.

Schroedinger's equations grapple with the problem of relating cause and effect in a world which is governed by Heisenberg's principle. They tell us that it is impossible to predict with precision what will be the outcome of an event on the atomic scale. The most that can be done is to establish the various possible outcomes and to assign to each of them the probability of that being the result which will eventuate.

It was Schroedinger's equations which led Einstein to make his famous protest that he could not believe that God played dice with the Universe. But it did not take him long to accept that what Schroedinger had shown was correct.

This principle of impossibility of prediction, which flows from Schroedinger's work, has given rise to much debate and experimentation. The trouble is that it is so difficult to relate such a principle to one's everyday existence. It has given rise to such questions as: where is the electron when it has a 40% probability of being in one place and a 60% probability of being in another? It has even given rise to a debate as to whether something is happening which seems impossible in the light of what Einstein said about General Relativity. Such debates are far from being settled.

In everyday life, we do not need to be concerned about such debates. It is enough to recognise that the Universe is under-pinned by concepts which we can understand in themselves; but which,on their face, do not seem to have much to do with the world as we perceive it with our five senses: in fact, they do.

There is another principle of quantum mechanics which some think is more fundamental than the principles already dis-cussed: it is called 'complementarity'.

It is known that light can manifest itself either as a wave or as a particle. In particular, if you shine a beam of light on to a plate with two parallel slits in it close together, the light will behave as a wave and produce interference fringes. That is to say, if the light then falls on a flat surface parallel to the plate, you will see bands of alternating light and dark. Those bands are them-selves parallel to the slits and they are brightest in the middle and get dimmer further out. This was Young's famous experi-mental proof that light is a wave.

On the other hand, light behaves quite differently if you shine it on the surface of a photoelectric material, as Einstein himself proved. It behaves like a particle.

However, light cannot behave as both wave and particle at the same time. It seems that the true view of the nature of light is that it is neither a wave nor a particle but 'a packet of energy which can be a wave or a particle but never both together'.

The same is true of an electron which is normally thought of as a particle but which can also behave like a wave, in which case it can show interference fringes.

Complementarity occurs in everyday life. A simple example is found in the tossing of a coin. It can fall heads up or tails up; but it cannot be both heads up and tails up at the same time. That impossibility is inherent in the nature of a coin. So it is with light and electrons: it is inherent in their nature that they can be either wave or particle; but cannot be both at the same time.

The fact that these principles operate at the atomic level does not mean that they are things of little importance to us as human beings. The changes which we call evolution are all initiated at the atomic level, because it is when the DNA in an egg or sperm, or seed, differs from that of its parent, that offspring are caused to have a different characteristic from that of their parents. Such differences can be caused by, among other things, the collision of a radioactive particle with a DNA molecule.

One result, at the human level, is that it is impossible to predict how and when any such change may occur. This is a further reason why it must be accepted that evolution is not a guided process but a random one.

Evolution has not come to a stop: it is very much alive and working today. The fact that human beings do not seem to have changed much over the years of history tells us nothing; because all our history is so short compared to geological time. The more complex the creature, the less easy is it for a change in DNA to be apparent. But when a study is made of small creatures such as bacteria, or even small flies like the fruit flies which are so frequently used in genetic experiments, it becomes apparent that evolution is at work all the time.

Also, it should be remembered that small changes in DNA, which may seem very small in relation to the human genome as a whole, can have a devastating effect on the individual. Examples which are now familiar include Huntington's chorea, spina bifida and cystic fibrosis. At what time in human history the changes occurred which led to these unfortunate ailments we do not know. But they are a warning that such things could happen again.

Another such warning lies in the spread of MRSA, methicillin resistant streptococcus aureus. This bacterium causes a most serious illness which is frequently fatal and cannot be cured by any known antibiotic. It was unheard of when penicillin first came into use. Since then it has emerged as a deadly bacterium; whether it did so by changes in its DNA, that is to say by mutation, or because it always existed and natural selection meant that it would grow better in the absence of competing bacteria which had been killed by antibiotics, is not clear. What we have learned is that antibiotics should not be used unless that is necessary.

We do not know if is possible to construct a universe that runs on other lines because we have never seen a universe run on lines other than those prescribed by Quantum Mechanics. And as Einstein has shown so clearly from Relativity, we cannot know what, if anything, may be happening outside our own Universe.

But we do now know some important things about our own Universe in addition to the small scale ones already mentioned. Thus we know that the Earth on which we live could not have been made 'in the beginning'; that is to say, at the moment in time at which the Universe itself was made.

Most of the matter in the Universe is hydrogen; there is quite a lot of helium, but very little of any other element; this we know from the work of astronomers. When hydrogen condenses, under the influence of gravity, into stars, and gets hot as our Sun has, it begins to make other elements including helium and carbon. But a star like our Sun cannot make the heavier elements with which we are so familiar, such as iron, which is essential to haemoglobin and thus vital to our existence.

Those elements are made only in a supernova. That is a star which is about 100 times as massive as our Sun. It burns its hydrogen for some millions of years, turning it into helium, and then it starts to burn the helium which it has made from the hydrogen. All this it does because its enormous size causes gravity to produce intense heat and pressure inside it. That goes on for a few more million years until suddenly the star collapses and then explodes. It becomes the brightest thing in the sky; it collapses in a fraction of a second. The temperature and pressures are so enormous that it makes those heavy elements and blasts these materials into space at a fantastic velocity.

Unlike most other stars, our Sun contains some of these heavy elements; as does the Earth. The only place such heavy elements can have come from is a supernova. So we are forced to conclude that our Earth is made of the detritus which was dispersed by the explosion of a supernova and which has come together again under the influence of gravity; possibly because the Sun passed through a cloud of such detritus.

One result is that we now know that our Earth cannot have been formed until the Universe was already some thousands of millions of years old. Furthermore, the inference is inescapable that our Earth was not created as suggested in Genesis. It came into being as an accident because a passing star happened to go through that detritus.

The story of a supernova identified as 1987A furnishes remarkable confirmation of these assertions. Quantum Mechanics predicts that a supernova will eject enormous quantities of a particle known as a neutrino, which will then travel at the speed of light. If that is right, one would expect that some neutrinos from the supernova would arrive at the Earth at the same time as the light from it.

1987A was first noticed by an amateur astronomer in Australia. He immediately told a professional friend, who alerted the astronomical world to such an important event. Many of them had had automatic photographing telescopes, which marked the exact time of each photograph. Those who had them pointing at that part of the sky examined their photographs. By working backwards on the time scale of their photos, they were able to establish the time when light from 1987A first arrived here. At two places in the world there were experiments running, for other purposes, which were considered capable of recording the passage of a neutrino. They had computers taking regular records of these experiments which, again, recorded against time. When those records were examined, they showed several instances of the passage of neutrinos and of the first ones passing at exactly the same moment as the light was first recorded by the telescopes.

It is obviously impossible for an astronomer to generate such an experiment as a supernova in order to test his theories, but he can use the phenomena which it produces as a check upon his scientific understandings and the predictions based upon them. And so he can use them as a check upon the theories on which he based his predictions. It is very satisfying to find such confirmation of a theoretical prediction in a situation in which the scientist has not set up the experiment in question. In that respect, it has similarities with the famous occasion when Einstein's prediction that the gravitational pull of a star would bend light passing close to it was verified during an eclipse of the Sun.

Quantum mechanics has moved a long way beyond the simple principles already discussed. It has moved into the area of the relationship between the constituent parts of an atomic nucleus, that is to say, of protons and neutrons. It has also probed, with success, into the constituent parts of each of those particles. As a result, physicists have developed Quantum Electrodynamics and Quantum Chromodynamics. They have discovered quarks, the strong force and the weak force. Furthermore, the interrelationship of these forces and particles is now well understood. Some parts of that knowledge were involved in the prediction referred to above about neutrinos and a supernova.

There is still much to be learned but there are two intriguing puzzles which are worth mentioning. The first is concerned with the breakdown of radioactive atoms; the second with the nature of gravity.

It is widely known that, if one has a piece of radioactive material, its atoms will regularly split and emit radioactive particles. It splits so regularly that, for each such material, we can assign a period of time which is called its half life. During the half life, half of the original atoms in a given sample will have split; after the passage of another period of time equal to the half life, half of the remainder will have split; and so on. Once the half life has been ascertained, one can predict accurately how much of an original piece of material will remain after a stated period of time. What has so far proved impossible is to predict which atom, out of the many in a sample, will split next; and to increase or decrease the half life.

Quantum mechanics has not yet found the answer to these puzzles. We have a little knowledge about the second one from the operation of nuclear reactors. We know that Uranium 235 can be made to split more frequently in the presence of slow neutrons and can turn Uranium 238 into Plutonium: but, at present, there is no generally worked out understanding of why these things happen, which can be applied to other radio-active materials. A solution to these puzzles would be of great value: apart from anything else, it would teach us how to dispose of the radioactive by-products of nuclear reactors; and perhaps to generate power while doing so.

This may seem to be the imaginings of science fiction. But, before such thoughts are rejected, it is worth looking back into the 19th century. Who would have believed, from what was known of electricity and magnetism, and the nature of matter, in that century, that the future would hold the technologies of radio, television, radar, X-rays, calculators, computers, mobile phones, the internet and much else that is based on our knowledge of electro-magnetism and Quantum Mechanics?

Many physicists have been studying the problem of finding a formulation which would embrace gravity as well as the known aspects of quantum mechanics. Various ideas have been floated. Verification of them calls for the ability to subject atomic particles to very high energies. Such energies are very difficult to achieve; and the equipment for achieving them very expensive to build and run. The lessons of the past ought to have taught us that what is perceived today as the pursuit of academic knowledge, having no apparently useful value, may lead to-morrow to the realisation of end results of great value to us all.

Some of the last part of this chapter may seem to have little relevance to theology. However, its significance will become apparent later.

5

Cosmology

The reason for looking at this topic is to consider the question whether God was the originator of this Universe. Did He originate it? Or did it happen in some way we do not yet understand but which did not involve the intervention of a supernatural being, such as God? This is one of the basic questions which divides the atheist and the theist.

The twentieth century has produced an astonishing growth in the understanding of the nature of this Universe, how it began, what drives it and where it seems to be going. Two aspects of that growth are particularly important.

First is the discovery that quantum mechanics underlies all the activities of atomic-size particles. This has given us an understanding of how the stars derive their energy, and much besides which has already been considered.

The second is the collection of advances in the field of astronomy. Perhaps the most important, for present purposes, were two discoveries by Edwin Hubble in the 1920's. The first is that many of what seemed to be points of light in the sky are, in fact, agglomerations of millions of stars forming a galaxy. We live in a galaxy. We are near the outer edge. It contains millions of stars. On a clear night you can see it with unaided eyes, edgewise on, as the Milky Way. It is now well established, thanks to the developments in telescopes, both in visible light and other forms of radiation, that there are millions of galaxies. More accurately, millions of galaxies have already been charted. How many more lie beyond our present limits of vision nobody knows.

At the sort of distances that these galaxies are seen, distance is measured in light years. A light year is the distance travelled by light, which travels at 300,000 kilometres per second, in one year. Since a year contains more that 31 million seconds, a light year is almost 10 million million kilometres. These astronomical distances are so large as to be difficult to grasp. Even more so when you realise that the furthest galaxies are millions, if not billions, of light years away.

There is another aspect of the great distance to those galaxies. The fact that they are millions of light years away means that the light which reaches us is millions of years old. What we see, or otherwise detect, shows us what that part of the Universe was like those many millions of years ago: not what it is like at those distances today.

Edwin Hubble made another surprising discovery. He measured the colour of the light coming from different galaxies. He found what he called a red shift: that is to say, that the light from the more distant galaxies is redder than the light from the nearer ones. He also found that there is a linear relationship between the distance and the degree of red shift.

His interpretation of these facts is now fully accepted as correct. The Universe is expanding and the farther away from us any particular galaxy is, the faster it is moving. This means that the Universe is expanding, more or less uniformly, in all directions.

If that is so, it invites the question: what was it like in the past? One way of thinking about that is to think of the Universe as being on a cinema film which is run backwards. The obvious conclusion is that, if the expansion is uniform, at some time in the past, everything in the Universe was at a single point; and that it has been expanding ever since. This idea was initially ridiculed by some physicists, including Fred Hoyle, who believed that the Universe was in a steady and stable state; and that matter was being continuously created in the space between the galaxies. They coined the name 'Big Bang', which was intended as a derisory name for a concept which they regarded as ridiculous. They were wrong; no evidence of continuous creation has ever been found. The name has stuck; and the concept of the Big Bang is now regarded as correctly indicating what happened.

The Big Bang occurred some 12 to 15 billion years ago. It seems that, at that moment, there was no space and no time. Then an explosion occurred, of what, in everyday terms, is an infinitely large amount of energy which then started to expand, thereby carrying the framework of space-time with it. As it expanded, a moment came when the energy started to yield matter. Einstein's $E=mc^2$ works both ways. An amount of energy E is equal to an amount of mass E/c^2. So some of the energy began to turn into mass. Throughout this time the expansion was taking place. As the mass began to appear, gravity began to act upon it.

If you wish to know all about what happened and has been happening since the Big Bang, there are many books to inform you.

What is remarkable, for present purposes is that the rate of expansion of the Universe, the strength of gravity and various other constants of the Universe, are just right to enable life to exist, and us to be here to have a look at it all and to think about it all. Again, there are books which can give you all the details about those things. One or two examples will help to make the point clearer.

Let us first look at gravity. We know that the strength of gravity is proportional to the inverse square of the distance between the two bodies whose gravitational attraction is being considered. Now consider a piece of mathematics worked out by Newton. He said that, if one point is revolving in a circle about a centre, the moving one is undergoing an acceleration towards the centre proportional to the square of the radius.

Now consider the Earth going round the Sun. Suppose that gravity became a little stronger than it is: would not the Earth spiral inward toward the Sun? And if it were weaker: the reverse? So we see that the strength of gravity is just right to keep the Earth moving in a circle (actually ellipse, but the mathematics is the same) around the Sun. And the same is true of every body orbiting another. Were things otherwise what would have happened? There would be no orbiting. Either there would be a solid lump of a Universe or a diffuse fog.

Consider the matter of the expansion of the Universe. Those who have worked on that have said that if the expansion rate were significantly faster there would not have been enough time for gravity to cause galaxies and stars to form. In contrast, they say that if gravity were significantly stronger, the galaxies would be too hot and dense for us to live.

Then there are a lot of numerical constants which, when applied to various formulae tell us a lot about our world. For example, one such constant controls the valency of the elements; that is to say the number of those electrons attracted to the nucleus of an atom, which are free to be attracted to the nucleus of another atom, and so able to make two or more atoms join together to make a molecule.

Carbon has a valency of 4 and this is crucial to the existence of life because it permits the formation of the chains of carbon atoms which make possible the proteins and other substances which underlie the existence of life.

Thus far, the scientists are in agreement. It is when they ask the question 'why does this happen to be so?', that disagreement emerges. Some say that it is just a matter of probability whether such constants have one value or another; that would mean that it is just a matter of luck that life, and us, are possible. Others say that the explanation is that there are many universes, each having values different from the others and that, of course, we have the one with those critical values. Otherwise we would not be here to ask the question.

Then there are those who say that all these facts are evidence of deliberate design, especially when one also remembers the use of quantum mechanics and gravity as the driving forces of the Universe. So they say that such things show that there must have been a designer: a supernatural entity: in other words, God. Thus, we do have here facts which are consistent with the concept of God as the originator and designer of the Universe.

There is a further problem which has to be confronted by those who argue for a purely physical cause of the Big Bang. What preceded it? Was it a Big Crunch? If so, what preceded the Big Crunch? And so on. In other words, if one argues for a purely physical origin to the Universe, one gets caught in an infinite regression: an endless sequence of physical acts, each preceding the other. But how did the first one get started?

So one is faced with a dilemma. If one thinks it was all designed, one accepts that there was a designer: God. But if one thinks not, then one has an infinite regression and no explanation of how the first thing, whatever it was, came about. Of course, the fact that we do not know the answer to that question now does not mean that there is no answer.

Whether, and if so when, there will be a resolution of the debate nobody can, at present, say. There are opinions and beliefs but no proof.

It is to be noted that there is no clear and acceptable evidence that God does not exist. Equally, there is no clear and acceptable evidence that He does. It is worth remembering, in respect of both propositions, the old tag that absence of evidence is not evidence of absence. That is why I call myself an agnostic; that is to say, one who does not find the evidence, which we have at present, compelling either way and so keeps an open mind.

At this point, it is appropriate to administer a caution: even if God created the Universe, it does not follow that He has done anything to it since then. Is it possible that he has just left it to run under the rules and with the energy with which He started it and done nothing to interfere with that? Is He, today, an observer rather than an active participant?

Perhaps the right inference is that the Universe may, indeed, have been designed and originated by God; but that his attitude towards it is that, having set it up, defined the principles on which it is to run and endowed it with a liberal quantity of energy, thereafter He leaves it to run in accordance with the laws which govern it. In other words, His attitude towards this Universe may be the same as that of a child who sets a top spinning, stands by and watches it continue under the energy which he initially put into it and under the laws which govern spinning tops, until it runs down and topples over.

Neither intervenes.

As soon as you ask whether God has intervened since the Big Bang, you run into some problems. Suppose, as indicated above, the Earth was not created, but arose from the detritus of a supernova. Did God have a hand in shaping it, or ordering it in any way? Is it as it is today solely because of the natural forces of tectonic plates, weather, etc? Bearing in mind also the consequences of what Darwin taught is there any scope for a proposition that God had a hand in making us what we are?

45

It is one thing to say that God started the Universe, but it is another to say that He has ever done anything since except watch what happens.

6

Prayer

Many people who believe that God exists also believe that He plays a part in the daily life of this Universe, and in their own daily lives. Some of them are scientists who, as a result of their teaching and experience as scientists, are not satisfied of the truth of a proposition unless there is evidence to support it. This places them in a dilemma between belief and knowledge; and some seek evidence to support their belief.

It seems reasonable to infer that this is the position of Professor Russell Stannard who has published a book called *The God Experiment*. In it he describes a Prayer Experiment which was to be set up with the aim of testing whether prayer can be effective; that is to say, whether it can achieve anything.

The first time it was carried out it was, apparently, inconclusive. The Professor says that it is proposed to set it up again.

It is modelled on the lines of the method used by the pharmaceutical industry to check the efficacy of a new medicine. Such a new medicine goes through many laboratory tests and, if it passes them, must then be tested on human volunteers.

A problem which arises in such tests is what is called 'the placebo effect'. If a patient is given a medicine and told that it will cure something or alleviate pain, or whatever, it will be found that, in a significant number of cases the condition of the patient will be improved, even if the 'medicine' which he is given contains nothing more effective than sugar. It is a fact that the mind can exert such force over the body that believing what the doctor says can influence the effectiveness of what is administered.

The method used to minimise this problem is sometimes called a 'double blind' method. It is designed to prevent any influence on the patient of any information which he, or the doctor administering the medicine, may have about the test. The patients are divided into two groups and each patient is identified only by a number. One half of the patients are given the new medicine and the other half has a placebo. Only the person in charge of the experiment knows which patient has which substance. All the patients, and the doctors treating them, are told that they are having the new medicine. When the effects on the patients have been evaluated, the person in charge can work out the extent to which the new medicine has proved useful. In doing so, he will have to discount those patients who display the placebo effect.

A similar procedure is proposed for the Prayer Experiment. A number of patients who are to have cardiac surgery are to be divided into two groups. One group is to be the subject of prayer by a number of people each of whom agrees to pray for a numbered patient. The person praying does not know who he is praying for and none of the patients knows whether or not he is the subject of prayer.

When all the surgery is completed, the patients are interviewed and asked about their experiences. It then falls to the person in charge to relate those experiences to the question whether the patient was, or was not, the subject of prayer.

What is remarkable about this endeavour is that nobody concerned with it seems to have addressed his mind to the assumptions which necessarily underlie the proposed procedure. They are such as to make the whole exercise pointless. Here are the necessary assumptions:-

1. God has the power to influence the outcome of surgery on a patient, of any complications, of any medication, etc.; and to do so by means which either do not involve human intervention; or cause such intervention without the doctor or other attendant being aware that God is intervening. In other words, He can do so, whenever He wishes, and by means which are as obscure to us as a conjuring trick.
2. He does not bestow this benefit on all and sundry, automatically and every day of the week; although, if He is all-powerful as is believed by Christians, He could presumably do so.
3. He only uses this power when prayed to. If not prayed to,

He sits by and lets the natural laws take effect. In other words, He deliberately allows patients to suffer despite the fact that He could assist them to get better; and He does so simply because He has not received a prayer for the patient with that particular number.

4. When prayed to He functions like any money-in-the-slot machine: put in a prayer with somebody's number on it and out comes a benefit for the person identified by that number. He exercises no judgement as to whether to function or not.

It is no good mincing words. If those are not the underlying assumptions, the experiment is pointless because it cannot otherwise yield results which can be used to evaluate the power of prayer. As in the pharmaceutical field, all extraneous influences must be excluded, or the trial will not yield useful information. The reason for saying that is that, if those assumptions do not hold good, it will be impossible to decide whether a person who gets better was helped by prayer; or a person who does not get better suffered because he was not prayed for. If a person gets better when God intervened without there being a prayer – or failed to get better when prayed for, because God decided not to act – it is bound to invalidate the results.

I ask in passing: Do you view God as acting like that? I will return to this topic when talking about miracles.

A further interesting consideration flows from the foregoing. The use of the double blind system shows a concern that, in its absence, the placebo effect might falsify the results. Why should that be thought possible? You have my deduction set out above. But, have you observed that, implicit in the concern which led to the use of that system, is the recognition that prayer may not be the cause of an effect which might be thought to be the result of prayer? I apologise for a convoluted sentence, but that conclusion must follow. This leads on to an implicit acknowledgement that prayer may have effect, not because God intervened to produce a result, but because such a result may be produced by the simple fact that the person prayed for *believes* that God is doing something to help (note the emphasis).

In other words, that it is the belief itself in prayer which is effective when effect occurs, not God's response to the prayer.

Those who designed the Prayer Experiment may not have appreciated that they ran the risk of shooting themselves in the foot.

The foregoing is concerned, as the Prayer Experiment was, solely with the possible effect of the prayers on someone other than the person praying. The prayers of a person for his own benefit raise a whole set of different considerations.

It is well known that any form of meditation can improve a person's ability to deal with a particular situation. I suggest that the prayers of such a patient for assistance for himself, if improvement results, achieve their result, not because of the intervention of God, but because of the ability of the human mind to affect the behaviour of the human body; indeed, of the whole person. The placebo effect is a simple example of this ability.

Others have suggested that the placebo effect can occur whenever three sets of circumstances come together: something which is thought to be effective; belief in the effectiveness of that something; and an authority figure whose authority reinforces the belief. Examples are: the pill or the prayer; belief in that; and a doctor or a priest. This suggestion also furnishes an explanation for the consequences which sometimes follow the 'laying on of hands' and spiritualistic séances.

The late, and much lamented, Formula I racing driver, Ayrton Senna raised an interesting question about the effect of prayer on the person praying. He let it be generally known that, before each race, he offered up to God a prayer for His assistance. We cannot know what he had in mind. But it seems wholly unacceptable to suggest that God poked His finger through the clouds and interfered with the fair running of the race. If all contestants prayed, would one of them beat Ayrton Senna? Or would God have been selective in his assistance?

I suggest that, if the praying assisted Ayrton Senna, it was because of the impact of meditation on the ultimate problem of the racing driver. Of course, he relies on the designer of the car, on the engineers who build it and set it up, and on the staff who change tyres and fill the car with fuel in the pits. But when it comes to driving the car, he is entirely on his own.

Those cars can do 200mph on the straights but, when the driver comes to a corner, he has to brake and reduce his speed to maybe 70mph or even 40 mph before accelerating away again. If he goes just a fraction too fast round the corner, the forces on the car will overcome the adhesion between the rubber of the tyres and the tarmac of the track. When that happens, the car slides; usually, it turns round and goes backwards. As a result, the car is likely to leave the track. If he is unfortunate, the driver will get stuck and be out of the race. If he is fortunate, he will manage to keep the engine going and get back on the track. Even then he has lost valuable time. The importance of even a little lost time can be seen from the fact that, even in a race of 2 hours, the winner may win by only a few seconds. The winner will be he who is able to drive just that little bit faster than everyone else without having the car slide off the road.

That is only one of his problems. Others include working out how and when to overtake, or avoiding another driver who may be having trouble keeping control of his car.

I suggest that, if Ayrton Senna's prayers really helped him, it was because they enabled him to focus his mind on the task in hand, to ignore such things as tiredness and discomfort, and to 'feel' the way the car was behaving so as to be able to drive it just that little bit faster than everyone else.

Is that explanation not preferable to the thought that God, when prayed to, would interfere with the fair running of the race? And is that not the more likely explanation of the fact that when somebody prays for himself or, to his knowledge, is the subject of prayer by those who know and love him, his mind may more strongly dominate his condition?

It does not seem that there is, or is ever likely to be, any evidence that prayer can affect the outcome of an event otherwise than by its impact on one who prays, or knows that he is the subject of prayer.

There are two more aspects of prayer worth looking at. One is the type of general prayer for someone in a public position; e.g. the prayers frequently said for the Queen and the Royal Family at Anglican church services. They know that prayers are said for them. Do those prayers have any effect? If they do, can any such effect be separated from the impact of the fact that they know they are being prayed for?

The second kind is the very general prayer, e.g. for 'those in peril on the sea'. How would one perform an experiment to check that such a prayer assists those in such peril? Does such a prayer cause God to assist sailors in a way in which He would not assist them without the prayer? If so, does He assist only those who are specifically named in the prayer; or does He assist all sailors equally? If He is able to assist all sailors equally, why does he wait for a prayer before doing so? Does such a prayer do anything other than make the congregation feel good?

In Chapter 1 I mentioned the matter of sacrifices; later I draw attention to the fact that the Jews practiced them e.g. Abraham and Isaac. The subjects of prayer and sacrifice lead me to ask a question.

Is there any real difference between these two beliefs:-

(a) the belief that a god will know that a sacrifice has been made and will regard it as accruing to one's benefit and
(b) the belief that a god will know that a prayer has been prayed and will regard it as accruing to one's benefit?

Both depend on the assumption that the god will be aware of the act in question; and that the god is so fully aware of the existence of the individual concerned so as to take note of the act and place it to that individual's credit. Are those assumptions justified?

The major religions no longer use sacrifice except in the form of individual self-denial, e.g. Ramadan and the Christian who fasts during Lent. But prayer remains a central part of all religions.

Could it be the fact that prayer has no effect except as a form of meditation for the person praying and, perhaps, in a similar way, for those who know that they are being prayed for?

Those who have faith will believe that their prayers have a real value to their god. This is, presumably, the thinking of those monks who pray, day in day out, for the human race. Do they think that their god will be pleased with them and be more kindly inclined towards the human race?

And, as suggested above, those who have faith that their prayers will be answered by God, either for themselves or a loved one, may well persuade themselves that God has answered.

The unanswered question is whether belief and fact go together.

Does not this discussion of prayer support the suggestion that, even though the Universe may have been started by God, there is no reason to think that He has intervened since?

7

Miracles

Like the previous chapter, this one deals with an aspect of the question whether the God who created the Universe, leaves it alone to run according to its laws; or interferes with that running, either of His own motion or when called upon to do so.

What are being dealt with here are those events which are properly described as miracles in accordance with the definition found in the Shorter Oxford English Dictionary:-

> A marvellous event exceeding the known powers of nature, and therefore supposed to be due to the special intervention of the Deity or of some supernatural agency.

Necessarily, they have to be considered against a background of a God who is assumed to have brought them about. Here a word of caution is necessary. One commonly thinks of the word 'miracle' in terms of beneficial events such as the cure of an illness. However, it must be remembered that a miraculous event could be any event for which there seems to be no natural explanation; and thus, an event could be considered to be a miraculous use of God's power by someone who observed an event which amazed him, but which he did not understand. Such a case is mentioned in the next chapter: the Indonesian fisherman who did not understand the cause of the 2004 tsunami.

So, in considering miracles, we are generally considering the question whether God intervenes at all in the day to day running of the Universe: that is to say, whether He is a participant or just an observer.

Miraculous events seem to have an important place in the beliefs of a Christian, especially among the Catholic community, among whom it appears to be believed that miracles are taking place in the here and now. Miracles have some place in the history of Judaism, that is to say, in the Old Testament: they do not seem to have any place in the day-to-day activities of contemporary Jews. Nor do they seem to have any importance in the beliefs of Muslims: although they believe that Abraham encountered the ram in the thicket, and that Allah spoke to Mohammed. There are many supernatural events in the tales of the Hindu religion; and their gods include ones whose appearance is not recognisably human, e.g. Ganesh and Kali.

What I propose to do is to examine the evidence for and against the view that miracles have occurred and do occur.

The Jewish tales of miracles all date from a long time ago. They include such tales as that of Moses striking the rock for water, of the falling of manna, of the crossing of the sea, of the fall of Jericho, and of the ram caught in the thicket when Abraham was about to sacrifice Isaac. The first four have this distinction from the last: that they relate to events which were conducted on a large scale in human terms as opposed to those which only affect one or a few individuals. There are many such large scale events reported in the Jewish scriptures but they all come from writings of which it is impossible to be sure that they were contemporary with the event, or even nearly so. Indeed, many scholars say that the writings came as long as centuries after the events said to be recorded.

Modern scientific knowledge tends to cast doubts on the authenticity of these tales. To take an example, consider the story about the fall of the walls of Jericho. The Biblical tale says that that was accomplished by walking seven times around the walls and blowing trumpets. It is known that the valley of the Jordan is a continuation of the Rift valley of Africa and has suffered many earthquakes in the course of its history. Such happenings as the fall of such walls might be attributable to earthquakes. There are other problems. One is that the dates do not tally: Joshua lived many centuries after any possible date for the fall of Jericho. Another is that, according to *The Unauthorised Version* by Robin Lane Fox, there is no archaeological evidence for the existence of a wall. One cannot help wondering what the truth is.

Strictly physical explanations have been put forward for the striking of the rock by Moses. In Palm Valley in the Finke Gorge National Park in Australia, the rock walls of the valley can become saturated with water, which has percolated down from above, to such an extent that water will flow from the rock. This is so despite the fact that the valley is in what seems to be a desert location, in that the land above the walls of the valley is desert. Did Moses encounter such a phenomenon?

One must also beware of falling into the trap of supposing that one has explained a miracle in terms of modern physics while claiming to retain God's intervention as an explanation. In Exodus, the crossing of the sea is attributed to the waters being divided by a strong east wind. It is logically inconsistent to accept that there may be a rational physical explanation for the manner in which a strong east wind was able to divide the waters, and still maintain that there was a miracle, unless one is prepared to grapple with the question: how did it come about that the wind blew in that way at that moment and then stopped so as to trap the Egyptians? Rabbi Goldberg said in an article in *The Independent* newspaper in 1993:-

> It was not God, but a strong east wind, *arriving at just the right moment*, over the Sea of Reeds, which enabled the Israelites to cross but submerged the Egyptians. (Emphasis added).

However, the problem of whether or not God intervened is not removed by substituting a reference to the sea, by one to the wind. The problem remains: did God, whether directly or by controlling the wind, cause the sea to separate at just the right moment? How often does the wind blow so as to cause the sea to separate? Should it be expected to do so when it did? Was it a fortunate co-incidence for the Israelites, that it blew to let them across and then stopped to frustrate the Egyptians? Or is the story a myth which has no foundation in fact?

In assessing the manner and extent, if any, to which God intervened in a miraculous way in the distant past, one can look for guidance from what is known to have happened, or not happened, in the present and the more recent past.

But first, mention should be made of another statement by Rabbi Goldberg in the same article:-

> We cannot imagine that even God can make a part equal to the whole, or the diagonal of a square equal to one of its sides, or two contradictory propositions valid at the same time·

These propositions bear a close similarity to the propositions mentioned in considering the consequences of Quantum Mechanics; in particular, Complimentarity. Is the Rabbi agreeing that God cannot make a coin fall both heads and tails at the same time, nor cause light to manifest itself as both wave and particle at the same time? Is he saying that God has no power to do anything which would conflict with the laws of Quantum Mechanics? If so, is there an inconsistency between the limits which he says are placed on God and his assertion that God is free to work miracles?

To what extent, if at all, is it possible for God to command the physical world to disobey the laws of Quantum Mechanics; or to disobey any of the principles of the laws of nature?

How far has He precluded Himself from doing that which cannot be done in the normal world?

Elsewhere in the article, Rabbi Goldberg appears to accept that it is possible for God to raise a person from the dead. He fails to grapple with the questions inherent in such a proposition: e.g. how long after death can God still do it? We now know that after approximately four minutes without an oxygen supply the brain will die; except in special circumstances, such as extreme cold. And we know that this is an irreversible process because the brain cells degenerate beyond the ability of the body to repair them. Can God raise a person from the dead after the body has become putrescent; or after it has rotted to the point of being only a skeleton? Can God bring back to life an Egyptian mummy?

These are serious questions, because they call into doubt whether, particularly in this field of resuscitation, God has unlimited power. Another reason why they are serious is because the Gospels report that Jesus brought a dead man back to life.

Assuming that some such incident really happened, how far gone was the corpse? Was the 'deceased' only in a state of coma? Did Jesus perceive this and use it for his own purposes?

If he did, it would seem to make a cynic of him. The visitor to Israel can be shown the place where this miracle is said to have occurred. But did it, in fact, occur?

There is abundant reason to doubt the miracles said to have occurred at Bethlehem at the beginning of Jesus's life as is indicated in *The Unauthorised Version* (ibid). Doubts on this issue have even been expressed by very senior members of the Anglican Christian hierarchy. The inconsistency here of the four Gospels is noteworthy. Similarly, doubts have been expressed about the blighting of the fig tree as being inconsistent with Jesus's character.

To return to the Old Testament for a moment, the tale of Abraham and Isaac is an odd one. What purpose could be served by having Abraham kill Isaac? Is the order to do so consistent with the present day concept of God as a God of Love? It is consistent with the old gods such as Baal and Moloch; just as it is with many other ancient gods such as those of the Aztecs. It is not consistent with God's law in the Ten Commandments that 'Thou shalt not kill'. It is also pertinent to ask: why did not Abraham defy Jehovah and tell him that, whatever the consequences to himself, he would refuse to kill another person; especially his own son? That is what God's own Commandment indicates as the right course to be followed. Perhaps that is what God expected Abraham to say and perhaps He then had to put the ram in the thicket in great haste to save Isaac's life.

Of course, one must be careful, in considering behaviour in ancient times to judge it by contemporary mores: not by those of today. And it was at a later date that the Ten Commandments were disclosed to Moses. Did God change his mind in the interim?

Muslims take a different view of this incident from that suggested above. They regard Abraham as a laudable individual because he was willing to obey God's orders despite the loss to himself of a son. They do not seem to think that Abraham ought to have refused to kill another human being.

There are practising Jews who regard the tale as allegorical rather than historical. They say that it represents the moment in time at which the Jews changed from making human sacrifices to making only sacrifices of animals. Such an explanation suggests that Abraham may have acted as he did because, at that date, human sacrifices were the norm. This may be so, but it suggests that the Jews formerly worshipped a God to whom human sacrifices were congenial; that the God whom they subsequently worshipped was content with the sacrifice of animals such as the ram caught in the thicket and, perhaps most importantly, that the God whom they now worship does not require that any creature be put to death in order to propitiate Him. Are those three the same God?

This raises the question whether God has, over the years, changed His mind about what we humans ought and ought not to do. Did He wish us to sacrifice then? Does He wish us to do so today? Or is it possible that the truth is something different: that we have, as we have learned more about the world in which we live, come to realise that mankind's earlier views about God and His requirements need to be revised? If it is the latter, we cannot afford to overlook the possibility that we may not yet have got it right and that there is still a lot to learn.

When one comes to the Gospels there is really only one miracle which can be said to be on the same large scale as the early Judaic ones referred to above: that is the feeding of the five thousand. The visitor to Capernaum will be shown the place where it is said that this miracle occurred.

At this point it should be noted that, even in the Gospels, it is nowhere clearly stated that Jesus considered himself to be more than a man. He was an orthodox Jew who, from his preaching in the Temple at Nazareth onwards, lost no opportunity to criticise the current practices of those in authority in the Temples. It may be commented that, in that respect, he was not unlike Martin Luther who took objection to the practices of the Roman Catholic Church in selling Indulgences. It seems that similar abuses were rampant in Jesus's time. Perhaps that was the prime source of Jesus's conflict with those in authority; and perhaps removing those abuses was the prime purpose of his activities. Such a view is certainly consistent with Jesus's expulsion from Nazareth and his departure to Capernaum; and with the hostility to him which culminated in the charge of blasphemy against him in Jerusalem.

Now let us look at more recent times. There seems to be no evidence of a recent miraculous event on a large scale such as the fall of the walls of Jericho or the parting of the sea. The world has seen many disasters and continues to see them. Wars apart, they are considered to be natural disasters, e.g. hurricanes, earthquakes, floods and volcanic eruptions. Some of the earlier ones such as the eruption of Krakatoa, and the burial of Pompei and Herculaneum, occurred in circumstance in which contemporary knowledge gave no forewarning and there was heavy loss of life. More recently, increased knowledge both about the causes of such phenomena, and how to circumvent their effects, has enabled loss of life to be reduced. This can be seen in the recurrent floods of Bangladesh, the earthquakes of California and Japan, and the hurricanes of the Caribbean. Today there is less loss of life when those events are compared with similar ones which took place even a few decades ago. In none of these events is it possible to discern the hand of God as taking any part, whether as a cause of the disaster, or in providing amelioration of its effects.

With floods in mind one may think of The Flood of Noah's time. This is reported in the Old Testament as being directly due to the hand of God. And when the waters had retreated, God made a covenant not to do it again, and sent the rainbow as a token of that covenant. There may be some fundamentalists who believe that all happened as so stated; and that there was no rainbow before the Flood. Modern knowledge of the physical causes of a rainbow makes it unacceptable to suppose that there was a time in the history of the Earth before which there were no rainbows, in the conditions of simultaneous rainfall and sunshine which cause us see them today. Likewise, it is unacceptable to suppose that the entire Earth was drowned in a flood. Recent research suggests that the Black Sea may have been a deep and populated valley which was flooded when the rising level of the Mediterranean broke through a land barrier. Was this the origin of the story of the Flood? If such tales as these are allegorical, or legends based on historical fact, how many of the miracles related in the Bible are to be taken as events which happened?

Coming to modern times, in the cathedral at Naples, in Italy, is a phial which is said to contain some of the blood of Saint Januarius. It is also said that, once a year on the anniversary of the Feast of Saint Januarius, it will liquefy and that, if it does not, the city will be overwhelmed by Vesuvius. This miracle is the subject of a very well attended service in the cathedral each year. It is always reported that the blood does liquefy.

There is no carefully considered evidence that what is reported by the priests is a liquefaction. There is, of course, no evidence that the contents of the phial are blood; let alone that it is that of Saint Januarius.

In the absence of any opportunity to explore the provenance of the blood of Saint Januarius, it is legitimate to take note of the results found when opportunity has been given to explore other allegedly miraculous happenings. An instance is found in the Turin Shroud. This is a large piece of cloth which bears a faint representation of what can be taken as a human face. It was said that this was the shroud in which Jesus was wrapped when taken down from the cross and that it bore, as a miraculous result, an impression of his face. In 1988, small samples of the fabric of the shroud were subjected to dating by the carbon 14 dating method and found to be not earlier than 14th century. In fact, this came as no surprise to those who knew anything about the shroud because it had been long ago conclusively proved not to have been what it was alleged to be. This, too, is dealt with in *The Unauthorised Version* by Robin Lane Fox.

So let us come right up to date. At Lourdes in the South of France is a grotto at which it is said, a young girl called Bernadette saw the Virgin Mary in 1848. This is a place of annual pilgrimage attended by many Roman Catholics seeking a cure for an illness or disability. From time to time reports of a cure, which is said to be miraculous, appear in the newspapers.

Such a one was reported in 1993 and was made the subject of a study by the Roman Catholic Church. It seems that that Church has no way, based on theological grounds, for determining whether such a cure is a miracle or not. Instead, the priests rely, for their proof that there was a miracle, on seeking to prove that it could not have been a natural cure.

Such an approach is wide open to criticism for two reasons. First is the difficulty which is always found in trying to prove a negative. The second difficulty exists because, in the present state of knowledge, no reputable medical expert will say that such a cure cannot have been natural. If he is a person of integrity, he cannot say more than this: that medicine does not *yet* know of a natural cure (note the emphasis). What he does know is that mankind is continually learning more about such matters and he keeps an open mind as to whether such a cure could arise without miraculous intervention. He will also, of course, be aware of the Placebo Effect. Despite this obvious defect in the church's case, the incident was published in the French newspaper Var-Matin for 13th September 1993, as being a case of the occurrence of a miracle.

The history of the growth of knowledge in medicine justifies the use of the word 'yet' in the previous paragraph, and requires a very cautious approach to the question whether a particular cure occurred because of divine intervention. For example, in the middle of the 19th century, the disease of consumption, as tuberculosis was then called, was debilitating at best, and frequently fatal: today, it is known to be caused by bacteria which can be brought under control by modern antibiotics. Similarly, infantile paralysis, as poliomyelitis was known in the 1930's, frequently led to people having to live in an 'iron lung' in order to stay alive, because the paralysis prevented them from breathing. Nowadays, those afflictions are both preventable and curable. Consequently, we now know that what might have seemed a miraculous cure of either of those diseases in the past, should not be categorised as miraculous today because one could not exclude the possibility that it was due to the patient's own immune system successfully prevailing against the causative organism.

Will a convinced Christian be persuaded by such an analysis as the above? Does he wish to believe that God can work miracles? And that Jesus did so? Does he have an emotional need to believe? The task of re-examining all that he has believed for so long may well be beyond him. Experience suggests that he will work hard to find ways of adhering to his beliefs and finding a niche in them for miracles.

On the one hand we have the person to whom faith is paramount. On the other, we have the person who puts any question of belief second and who brings his intellect to bear in order to examine the evidence. They may well reach different conclusions.

What is at issue is the fundamental theological question whether God has retained, and exercises, the power to interfere with the workings of the natural laws by which He has set the Universe to run.

Alternatively, as the atheist would ask, whether there is really a God who plays any part in the workings of this Universe.

8

Pain and Suffering

To many Christians, the existence of pain and suffering in this world poses a problem. They perceive the problem because they hold the view that God is a god of love. To them the problem is to understand how a God of love can permit the pain and suffering which exists in the world. Every time there is an appalling example of man's inhumanity to man, such as the brutal beating and torture of a young child, one hears the anguish in the voice of those who speak publicly of such things. The answer which is given is that God has seen fit to confer freewill on mankind and that such things are part of the penalty.

Let us look more closely at the ingredients of this problem and see whether 'problem' is appropriate, or even needed; we also need to consider what is really involved in freewill.

First a word about 'good' and 'evil'. These are commonly thought to be words which all will understand; but that is wrong.

They are not absolutes. They are words which state the appraisal by a particular culture of a particular set of facts. It is by no means unusual to find that what is thought to be good by one culture will be thought to be evil by another; and vice versa. This applies not only to cultures which are differently located geographically, but also sometimes to the same culture at different periods of time.

Some examples will illustrate the point:-

1. Everybody has heard of the Inquisition. Today, we of the west have no doubt that its practices were evil. Were they not considered good by the Vatican at the time those things were done? And remember that in those 16th and 17th century days, the Protestants practiced them as vigorously as the Roman Catholics.

2. When the British went to India in the 17th century they found a Hindu practice of suttee; the practice of a widow immolating herself on her husband's funeral pyre. There is no doubt that a widow who did that was considered good by Hindus; in some of the more remote parts of the country, it is occasionally practised today. The British found it abhorrent and did their best to stamp it out. They took the same view of the practice of Thuggee.

3. Slavery has been known throughout history. The Slave Trade, i.e. the catching of black Africans, and shipping them to the Americas was started by the Portuguese in the 15th century. It was approved by the Roman Catholic Church. In fact, the Pope divided the Americas between Spain and Portugal; and authorised those countries to operate their enterprises in the Americas by means of black slaves taken from Africa. The wealth of Bristol and Liverpool was founded on the Slave Trade. That trade has ceased to exist and today, slavery is regarded with revulsion by most of us.

4. When the Moguls invaded India, they built a mosque at Ayodyha on the site where the Hindus believed that the Lord Ram had brought mankind to the Earth. A few years ago, a mob of Hindus destroyed that mosque completely. Which of them was good; and which evil?

5. And remember the Islamists who terrorise and kill those of the West in the name of *Jihad*, a holy war authorised by Allah.

Such examples could be multiplied almost to infinity. What they teach is that the questions of pain and suffering must be looked at objectively: free of the obfuscation of a cultural assessment.

There are four classes of the causes of pain and suffering: accident; illness, including genetic defect; natural disaster; and man's inhumanity to man. What we are looking for is to find out whether it is right to believe that God has, or can be presumed to have had, any responsibility for these causes.

Accident

Accident is involved in an event for which the sufferer does not, or not always, carry a measure of responsibility: e.g. the innocent victim of another's bad driving of a car. One often hears the cry: why me? The answer is the simple one that, as a matter of probability, if several million cars are engaged in using a rather restricted set of roads, and sharing them with a lot of pedestrians and cyclists, someone is likely to make a mistake and someone is likely to be hurt. This is even more likely if some of them are irresponsible young people, or people on drugs or alcohol; or old dodderers. As to the identity of who is hurt, the answer is the simple, but brutal, one: the person who had the misfortune to be in the wrong place at the wrong time. Scientific reasoning has established beyond doubt that much, if not all, of what happens in this Universe involves a measure of probability; remember what is said above about Darwin and Quantum Mechanics.

Consider this: in the United Kingdom we kill 3,000 people on the roads each year. Nobody can predict today who will be next year's victims, but the probability is so high that it can be stated as a statistical certainty that we will have killed another 3,000, give or take a few, by the year's end. Believers must accept that the impact of probability is involved in the nature of the Universe which their God has created. Perhaps there is no other way of making a Universe work.

Another cause of accidents lies in our persistent practice of not taking care when we do things; or doing things about which we do not have the necessary expertise. Hilaire Belloc coined a delightful verse on this theme:-

> Lord Finchley tried to mend the electric light
> Himself. It struck him dead; and serve him right.
> It is the duty of the wealthy man
> To give employment to the artisan.

Then there are the accidents due to simple carelessness, such as not setting up a ladder correctly. There are many such.

Illness

First, there is the obvious point that, if we did not feel pain when something is wrong with us, we would not know that something was wrong. From this point of view, pain is an essential survival mechanism; e.g. if you hit your thumb with a hammer, pain tells you that you have damaged it. What is interesting about the 'problem' is that that survival mechanism is also needed to cope with illness.

There is a variety of causes of illness: primarily parasites, bacteria, fungi, and viruses. As examples, one may mention:-

1. The plasmodium parasite responsible for malaria; tape-worms; and the filarial worms which cause elephantiasis.
2. Pneumococcus bacteria which cause pneumonia.
3. Fungi such as cause athlete's foot and ringworm.
4. Viruses such as rabies, measles and, discovered more recently, HIV which causes AIDS.

There is also a newly-encountered cause of disease, viz. a prion: it is thought to be the cause of BSE (the mad cow disease) and CJD (the similar trouble in humans). Then there are the illnesses which are caused by genetic defects.

If the question is to be asked 'How can God permit all this?', a good starting point is to look at what has been said about what He created and how He did it.

To the Christian and the Jew, the history of creation is set out in the first few verses of the Book of Genesis. There one is told what was done and when and, more than once, it is said that 'God saw that it was good'.

Let the obvious be stated. Nowhere in the Jewish Bible does it say that God created the parasites, bacteria, viruses and fungi; nor that He engineered the genetic defects. Still less that He thought any of it good. This is not a blasphemy; nor or a silly joke: it is a point of serious theological import. What is the theist to believe? Did God deliberately create them, if so when? Or were they the work of Satan? If neither, how does it come about that they exist?

Silence on this point in Genesis comes as no surprise to the scientist. At the time when Genesis was written mankind had no knowledge or understanding of any of such things; so the writers of Genesis did not have to consider them. The causes of disease were a mystery. Today, a very great deal is known.

Life does exist. It exists in an enormous variety of forms. It has existed for many millions of years. The only tenable inference is that it is an inevitable concomitant of the existence of life that it is possible for it to take the form of those parasites, bacteria, fungi and viruses. If what is known about this planet is to be taken as the judge, that is the only explanation. All palaeonto-logical research indicates that bacteria existed long before the more complicated plants and animals evolved.

Studies of these causes of illness show that the pathogen lives and multiplies inside, or on the skin of, the host which has the disease. The symptoms are caused in various ways e.g. by a toxic material which is secreted or excreted by the pathogen, or by the pathogen damaging the body's mechanism for subsist-ence or repair. Sometimes by causing the host's immune system to attack the host.

There is another way of looking at this question which has been rendered possible by modern knowledge of the workings of living things. It is this:-

> Every living thing is a chemical machine constructed and operated in accordance with the information contained in its DNA.

That may sound extravagant, but it is true. There is no such thing as a 'Life Force'. Every plant grows from its seed in accordance with the information contained in the DNA in that seed. The energy which it needs and uses is initially energy which was stored in the seed during the previous growing season; thereafter it is electrical energy derived from the action of sunlight on chlorophyll.

Members of the animal kingdom derive their energy from breaking down the materials which they ingest and using electrical energy from the chemicals thus obtained. A chemical called adenosine triphosphate is universally used in these electrical operations.

What is apparent from all that we know about living things, past and present, is that these chemical machines can exist in an enormous range and variety of forms. So it is no matter for surprise that some of them can do things which are inimical to our well-being, e.g. as pneumococcus does with the chemicals which it gets rid of as waste products from its chemical operations. They interfere with some of our chemical operations and cause pneumonia.

These conclusions are what one would expect from a full appreciation of what Darwin said about evolution and they remove from the field of debate the possibility that God deliberately created such things. However, the more strongly it is asserted that God is a God of love, the more inevitable becomes the conclusion that they exist because there is nothing that God can (or will?) do to control or inhibit them. And that seriously undermines the proposition that God is all powerful.

So the explanation is the simple one that, if life can exist, it can exist in forms which are regarded as undesirable by humans, as well as in forms which we regard as desirable. And it is worth remembering that we rely for our very survival on bacteria, e.g. those which live in the gut. Everything which we have learned from Darwin seems to make this answer inescapably correct. And if that is so, then we have no basis for puzzlement as to why God allows such things: they are as inseparable from our existence as our need to eat and breathe.

That brings me to genetic defects. That is a topic which could not have been talked about only a few years ago. Now, however, we know that DNA is the master blueprint for the construction of every living thing on this planet. An individual's DNA exists in every cell in the body. From the point of view of genetic defects the most important cells in the body are the ovaries and testes. It is in them that the DNA is prepared for transmission to the next generation. If it contains an error, that error can cause defects in the offspring without necessarily causing, or being allied with, any malady in the parent. That is why it is possible for a child to be born with a defect, the possibility of which the parents never suspected.

An example of such a defect is the one which causes cystic fibrosis. The symptoms are well-known. It is now understood that the defect consists of a single transcription error in just one letter of one triplet of the gene which directs the manufacture of a certain protein. It is a protein which is involved in the transmission of certain substances across the walls of cells. That error has the consequence that an incorrect amino acid is inserted at a particular place in the protein; as a result the protein is not what it should be and does not work properly.

It is also established that that error does not affect the child unless both parents have the error. If only one parent has it, the child will have one defective gene and one correct one and it will seem normal. But, apparently, such a child is capable of passing on the defect. The ironic result is that both the parents may seem perfectly healthy and have no idea that their children will be at risk. Furthermore, a child who has only one defective gene can be a carrier without suspecting it.

It is important, for reasons which will appear later, that such a defect is recognised as being an example of a past mutation which has not been eradicated by Natural Selection, even though it can produce offspring of an impaired survival potential. That is so because the defective gene can go on from generation to generation while only one parent has it. When both parents have it there is a probability that, of any children, they will be afflicted in the proportions that Mendel discovered: i.e. out of every four, 1 with 2 defects who is ill; 2 with 1 defect; and 1 with none. The defective gene only reduces survival potential when both parents have it. There are now known to be many such mutations which have survived because their presence does not always reduce survival potential.

The conclusion to be drawn for present purposes is that this type of defect is inseparable from the particular chemical method which is employed to pass on genetic information from generation to generation; and from the fact that the environment, in the form of radiation, or poisonous chemicals, or even just accidental errors in transcription of DNA, can cause mutations. When it is being used, DNA is transcribed by mechanisms in the cell into RNA. Errors sometimes occur in this process and in associated ones and those errors can lead to mistakes in the make-up of a protein.

Since it is those very phenomena which have made possible the mutations which led from the Earth's original bacteria to today's variety of species, it seems inescapable that the statement at the beginning of the preceding paragraph is correct.

Whether it might have been possible for the Universe to be constituted in such a way (whether you believe that it was done by God or otherwise) that some other method could be used, or for the origin of life and evolution to have developed something different, we do not know. But, since it is the method used for us, we must accept that the occasional presence of genetic defects is inseparable from our existence.

To sum up thus far, these illnesses and defects are part and parcel of the way a human being, and all life, is made. And it seems that the answer to the question why a God of love permits such things may simply be because there is nothing He can do about it, unless He is prepared to continually interfere with the laws according to which the Universe has been constructed: what we call the 'natural laws'. If that were to happen, how often would it happen? Would we find that miracles were a matter of daily occurrence to millions of people? If that happened, would those laws be any longer natural laws? Could we rely on them for any purpose – even boiling an egg? Would we be anything more than puppets of God?

As was suggested in the discussion of miracles, it does not seem wrong to say that God is in a dilemma between letting the world run according to the laws which He has seen fit (or been obliged- we know of no possible alternatives) to use; or continually interfering with it.

In short, do we suffer from these illnesses and genetic defects because there is no way in which we could exist without being prone to them? Or, as it is put above, because there is nothing God can do about it?

Either way, there is, in reality, no problem of pain and suffering under the head of illnesses; and no reason for believing otherwise.

In passing, it is interesting to note to what a large extent life is automatic. It is, of course, fully automatic for all plant and fungal life. Even in the animal kingdom, it is noteworthy how much of existence is automatic. Note these examples: your heart and its control, your digestion, your immune system, your repair system which heals when you are injured, your muscle control system and its sensory feedback. It is no matter for surprise that such complex regulatory systems sometimes go wrong.

Natural Disasters

The causes of most of the natural disasters are now fairly well understood. The heat of the sun warms the atmosphere, and the sea: but not evenly all over, because the sun only shines in daytime and shines obliquely at the poles. The resulting differences in temperature cause the winds; the winds pick up moisture from the seas; various complex phenomena cause heavy rainfalls, strong winds, storms, hurricanes, tornados and so on.

We know now about the movement of the tectonic plates on which the continents sit; about the resulting earthquakes and volcanic eruptions. There is reason to think that, without the tectonic plates life could not exist. This is so because of the contribution which the movement of those plates makes to mountain building, and therefore to the existence of dry land, and rainfall, and to the making of soil for plants to grow in by erosion of the rocks of mountains. So, again, we are forced to conclude that we only exist because these natural phenomena make it possible for us to do so.

Although the causes of those disasters are well known to the educated, such knowledge is far from universal. To many around the world, such things are still attributed to the local gods.

A particularly vivid example of this matter of attribution by an individual to his god appeared on television at the time of the tsunami of Boxing Day 2004. We were shown a devastated area at the shoreline somewhere in Indonesia and a local man, perhaps a fisherman, was interviewed. I do not recall his exact words but this was the effect of them:-

> 'I do not know why Allah has sent this terrible thing. I do not know why He has allowed it to kill my wife and children but leave me alive. Perhaps He has some purpose for me and perhaps I shall find it out.'

It is plain that, to that man, Allah was a real, live active participant in the daily life of his world: not only as a being to whom he prayed like a good Muslim, but also as a being who actually pulled the levers which made the world about him operate as he perceived it to operate day by day.

Such thinking is typical of the Biblical times as one can see from the Bible itself. To dispel it everywhere on this planet will be a long and arduous task.

All too often, it is our own fault that these natural disasters cause pain and suffering. We choose to live in places which are prone to disasters e.g. Los Angeles, the Caribbean islands, the slopes of volcanoes and places where storms can cause land-slides and flooding.

Accepting that these phenomena are an inevitable part of exist-ence means that there is no basis for blaming God for causing such disasters.

Man's Inhumanity to Man

This raises some different questions, because it raises acutely the issue of 'freewill'. The theist believes that this was a gift from God. But was it?

Let us start with some basic biology again. You know what an oak tree is (or whatever tree you are familiar with). You recog-nise one by its bark, its leaves, its acorns. Sometimes an oak tree is straight and tall: sometimes it is broad and spreading: but still plainly an oak tree.

But have you ever seen two identical oak trees?

There seems to be something in the genetic make-up of an oak tree which permits its branches and twigs to emerge at an apparently infinite variety of locations, and then to grow in an apparently infinite variety of different directions, and sizes and lengths: and yet it is still an oak tree. Have you ever noticed what a seemingly infinite variety of human faces there is, and that you are able to distinguish between them? And is it not interesting that we each have a fingerprint of such distinctiveness that the police can use them to catch criminals?

At the small end of the scale of the size of living things, all bacteria of a given species and variant may be identical. But at the large end of the scale, where the individual consists of a large number of cells, great variety is normal even within a species.

When we come to the animal kingdom, we find that variety can exist even within what is, in general terms, a common behaviour. Thus a given species of spider will build a given type of web. But the precise location and shape of the web are tailored by the spider. It might be thought to be attributing human thinking to the spider to say that it 'decides' where, and precisely how, to construct the web. But, if you examine an individual web, you will see a certain logic in the way that the spider has used the available twigs and grass as anchoring points for the web. This variety is analogous to the variety in the oak tree. But it is more than that: it is an indication that even a spider has 'freewill' when it comes to deciding what to do about a web.

So it is with all animals. The mating habits of sexually reproducing animals and birds indicate that they are carrying on a form of choosing which individual to mate with.

Watch a squirrel running about hunting for nuts, climbing trees, sitting up and testing a nut to see if it is good to eat. Are these not all manifestations of 'freewill'?

It seems as if this freedom of action is inseparable from the complexity of the life which we find in the higher organisms. The inference is that such freedom of action is unavoidable; that it is inseparable from what such animals are and, in our case, from what we are. In other words, that it has not been conferred on us humans alone, as a deliberate act by a God who chose it as an alternative from some collection of possible alternatives; but that we have 'freewill' because we cannot exist and not have it.

If this is right, there is no problem about man's inhumanity to man. It is inevitably possible for us to be harmful to one another; as well as to be co-operative. Whether, as individuals, we harm each other or not depends on a multitude of factors. Some of these may be genetic as in the case of a psychopath. Many lie in the nature of the culture in which we live; that is to say, in our non-genetic programming. That in turn seems to depend on the history of our culture. Nevertheless, if we observe the behaviour of animals, there is some reason to think that some elements of mutual co-operation are contained in our genes and have come about as a result of the effects of natural selection.

So, must we not conclude that the freedom to harm each other, or not to do so, is inseparable from the fact that the life which we have is ordered as it is? The question of the manner in which we use that freedom is dependent upon the rules which we have learned over the generations and built into our culture; and one of those rules is, of course, that we should train our young in the ways of that culture.

Whether that culture is based on religious or secular considerations is not relevant to that conclusion. The reason for saying that lies in what we know about various religions. For example, we have the teachings of Jesus; nevertheless, we had the Inquisition supposedly based on those teachings. To take another example of a religion, we had the worship of Quetzlcoatl by the Aztecs; to them a human sacrifice, from time to time, was a necessity.

Over the centuries, many people have written of ways of organising society. We, in the 21st century, are faced with the task of working out how society can be organised to the best advantage of all; and doing so in a globally organised world. Can we continue to tolerate the idea that that our society should be organised along lines laid down by somebody who lived years ago? Or along lines laid down in ancient texts? Is that not the root of Islamic terrorism? Is it not fair to say that only an approach along secular lines is capable of furnishing an acceptable compromise of the conflicting needs and wishes of the Earth's varied populations?

Whatever the future may hold there, on this head too of pain and suffering, there is no 'problem' for the theist and no reason for him to believe otherwise.

9

The Immanent God

The immanence of God refers to the concept that He is present in all parts of the Universe at all times; and, in particular, that He is present within each individual. So it includes a reference to that aspect of God which penetrates into the personal beliefs of the adherent to the religion: that is to say, the God to whom a person prays and who perhaps answers his prayers; or the God who does, or does not, work miracles for him; or the God who confers His blessing on those who seek it.

That is in contrast with the aspect of God already referred to as the designer and maker of the Universe, i.e. the Creator.

There is a consensus among Jews, Muslims and Christians that there is but one God. Despite that consensus, they are not in agreement as to the attributes and requirements of that one God. Indeed, there are a number of aspects of their different views of God which justify doubt as to the correctness of the concept of monotheism. Hindus are not monotheists but constitute so large a proportion of the world's religious adherents that they must not be left out of consideration. There are, of course, other religions such as Buddhism and Shintoism, but the above will suffice for a discussion of the problem involved in the concept of an immanent God.

Some say that science has no part to play in such matters: a point of view which may smack more of a refusal to face a possibility, than a conclusion based on reality. Furthermore, that view does not exclude the possibility that the scientific method of thinking may be able to throw some light. For one thing, it can stand back from all the religions and ask what facts ought to be considered and what questions the existence of those facts may give rise to. For another, it can try to answer those questions without any bias towards one view, or one religion, rather than another.

So, let us look at some of those facts and questions.

Ritual seems to be basic to all religions. But there are real differences between the religions as to what rituals should be observed. As examples mention may be made of the requirement for Jews to observe the Sabbath and Passover; for the Muslim, to pray five times a day, to take part in Friday Prayers at the mosque and to observe the Fast of Ramadan; for the Roman Catholic, there are genuflection, crossing oneself, confession and Hail Mary's; for the Protestant, there is the communal singing of hymns and the saying of prayers.

Another field in which significant differences exist is that concerning the changes which have taken place over history in the perceived requirements of the God of each of these religions.

At the time of Jesus the Jewish God was seen to require that an adulteress should be stoned to death. According to the Gospels, Jesus seems to have doubted the appropriateness of such a draconian punishment. At an earlier date Judaism employed animal sacrifices; and possibly human ones at an even earlier date. The modern Jew does not, apparently, think that adulteresses should be stoned to death, nor that sacrifices should be made. What is the significance of such changes?

At the time of Mohammed, Islam was seen to require that a thief should have his hand cut off and that an adulteress should be stoned to death. The Muslims of Saudi Arabia and those of Nigeria seem still to hold the same view. But those who have come to live in the United Kingdom do not take the same view. What is Allah thought to say today?

In the twelfth century a sect called the Albigensians took a different view from that of the Vatican on the nature of God. This led to them being stigmatised as heretics. Both sides claimed to be Christian. There was, of course, no way of telling which side was correct, or whether both were wrong. However, the Vatican took exception to the existence of that heresy and ordered the Albigensians to be slaughtered: and many thousands were. One cannot avoid the suspicion that that was an unwarranted misuse of religious power; probably, or at least possibly, in order to gain or hold secular power.

In those days the Roman Catholics thought that it was proper to slaughter the Albigensians and, through the Inquisition, to torture and burn to death those who disagreed with the view of the Vatican. They do not think the same today. Is it God who has changed, or have they changed their understanding of God? The present Pope has apologised, albeit very belatedly, for the Inquisition and for the treatment meted out to Galileo: what does that tell us? Should we infer that the alleged authority of the Pope has no real foundation?

A few centuries ago, the Protestants were also torturing people and burning them to death. They, too, have stopped doing so.

Today, some Protestants take the view that a priest may be a woman and that a priest may marry. Some Protestants have ordained women bishops: others refuse to accept that that is theologically proper.

On this aspect of affairs, the Vatican seems to be in a state of flux. To be ordained, a priest must be a man and be celibate. But they apparently accept as converts married men who wish to be priests. And there is reason to think that the issue of celibacy is under discussion.

Two thousand years ago, according to the Christians, God sent Jesus to the Earth to preach to all mankind. Jesus was crucified and, so it is said, subsequently ascended into Heaven. The Jews did not, and do not, think that He was the Messiah. Six hundred years later, according to Muslims, Allah sent the Angel Gabriel to Mohammed to disclose to him the Koran. There is a puzzle here if there is only one God: should we infer that God thought that the progress made from Jesus's teachings was unsatisfactory and decided to have another try at illuminating the mind of mankind? Are the Muslims wrong as to the source of the Koran? Is it to be believed that the God who sent Jesus was also the God who prescribed the penalties laid down in the Koran? Or is the Koran the work Of Mohammed; and not that of Allah? That last thought is intolerable to a Muslim.

There are interesting parallels between Judaism and Islam. Both called for stoning to death of adulteresses. Both proscribed the eating of certain meats; in particular, pork. In the climate in which both lived that was sound advice in the

79

absence of refrigeration. Yet both still have the same ban today. Similarly, Muslims only eat meat which is *halal* and Jews only that which is *kosher*. Sadly, the Muslims will not allow the beast to be stunned before its throat is slit. Would Allah really object to the use of this act of mercy which was not available 1400 years ago, but is today?

Then again, Allah ordered in the Koran that one hand only should be used for eating and the other only for bodily cleanliness. That was a rule which made sense in a desert environment where there was little water for washing. Does it make sense today, and should it be considered to be a directive of Allah which should be obeyed today in those technically advanced communities which have adequate washing facilities? Or would Allah allow a Muslim today to eat with either hand and to use toilet paper?

Outside the Mosque, in its forecourt, is a fountain at which ritual washing should take place. Again, to provide such facilities in the seventh century makes sense in a desert environment. Why the ritual washing today? And, having regard to what we now know of the prevalence of disease-causing bacteria, is it a wise procedure?

The Christian, at Communion, takes bread and wine as symbols of Jesus's body and blood. Some even believe in transubstantiation: that is to say, that the bread and wine change in their bodies into flesh and blood.

The Hindus worship several gods; and they had the practices of suttee and thuggee at one time. Why has God not disclosed to them the fact that He is only one?

How does it come about that a single God displays so much variety in what is required of those who worship Him; and so much change over the centuries of what those worshippers may, must, and must not, do?

Then there is the matter of conversion; that is to say, the changing by a person of his religion. Unlike a person's race and colour, which are determined for him by his genes and are for ever immutable, his religion is a matter of choice. He is likely to start off in life with the religion into which he was indoctrinated by his parents; or his school. But, once he grows up, there is nothing to stop him adopting a different religion (unless he is a Muslim, when he merits death for apostasy). Does he thereby change his God? Or does he do nothing more than change the club of which he wishes to be a member?

This leads to two questions. First, is whether God is, in truth, a being of external reality; that is to say, one who existed long before mankind evolved, and who will continue to exist long after mankind has gone from the Earth: this is the theism versus atheism point. Second is whether God actually does anything: or whether things attributed to him have other causes?

Various people from St. Thomas Aquinas onwards have struggled with these questions. In looking at them today we have the advantage of a much wider knowledge of so many things than was previously available.

A clue to a possible answer was contained in the BBC's Radio 4 'Today' program, in April 2002, in a slot named 'Thought for the Day'. The speaker (I believe it was the Rev. Colin Morris) was speaking about the impending speech of the Chancellor of the Exchequer in which he would disclose his Budget. The speaker said that the media would be talking of how the Budget would be received in the world at large by saying that 'the market will accept this . . .' or 'the market will reject that . . .' as if the market was a separate entity like a god. He then pointed out that what was called 'the market' was simply the consensus of view of a number of members of the community. After this, he referred to his own view about God which, as you would expect, was a normal religious one.

This leads me to ask whether it is possible that God is not a being of external reality but, like 'the market' is the name given to the crystallization of the consensus view of a community? Many will condemn such an idea as preposterous. Many will reject it out of hand because, to them, their God is real.

However, if such were true, it would explain much about the differences, and historical changes, noted above. It would cease to be a puzzle why a single God presided over so many different religions; why there were such great changes over the years in what was considered good by believers and what was not; why those of a given religion could disregard what others of that religion regarded as set in stone. All these different religions and practices would make sense if they were related to the characteristics of a particular culture and, therefore, not dependent on the existence of a single separate entity, namely God. It would then be apparent why nowadays God does not seem to perform miracles on a large scale but, if at all, only on a scale which is within the compass of individual humans, e.g. what are referred to as miraculous cures of illness.

It would explain why the God of Islam required conduct which was appropriate to a desert environment, but the God of the Christians did not. It would explain why it is possible for two sets of Christians to take such different views on so many topics. Indeed, it would explain much else.

It would not explain why so many people actually believe in the existence of a God: perhaps it is worthwhile exploring the possibility that the religious impulse comes from within, not from a God. There can be little doubt that the elimination of all these differences would go a long way to bringing consensus in place of the differences and disputes which so much beset this globalised world.

Do not be too ready to be dismissive of these ideas; instead, consider the history of witchcraft.

It was not so long ago that witchcraft was accepted by all and sundry as a matter of external reality. It was believed that witches were real and had supernatural powers with which to perform their evil acts.

Thus, they were accused of causing sows to become barren; of causing people to become ill; of putting a blight on crops; of causing storms and droughts; and even of killing people. And all that happened without the witch touching anybody.

It was firmly believed that this was not a natural power but a supernatural one. In Cromwell's time, the supernatural powers of witches were regarded so seriously that a Witchfinder General was appointed to flush out these witches. In England, and in Europe generally, the records show that many thousands of women were tortured, and hanged or drowned or burned to death for being witches.

As recently as 1877 five witches were burned alive in Mexico. And in England in 1890, it was reported at an inquest that a death had been caused by witchcraft.

Today the developed world knows that there is no such thing, in reality, as witchcraft; although in less developed countries there lingers a belief in shamans and witchdoctors. The belief in witchcraft was not, therefore, a belief in something which had external reality: it was nothing more than a consensual view held by a large proportion of the community. And it was a misplaced view which is seen today as unsupported.

It is worth noting, in passing, that it was largely, if not entirely, due to the efforts of scientists that it was learned that the phenomena, for which witches were blamed, were brought about by completely natural causes: illness and death by bacteria etc.; barren sows in the same way; storms and droughts by meteorological phenomena; and so on.

In short, phenomena which were at one time thought to be supernatural phenomena have come to be recognised as natural ones

What should we learn from this history of witchcraft? First, that it is easy, when people do not understand something, for them to attribute the cause to something supernatural. This aspect of human nature is illustrated by the incident of the Indonesian fisherman who assumed that the tsunami of 2004 was the deliberate work of his god (see chapter 8). Secondly, that, when we come to understand something, we should ask ourselves what our previous understanding of that phenomenon was. Thirdly, that when we have reviewed that previous understanding, we should ask ourselves whether there are other aspects of our beliefs about the world which ought to be reviewed.

I have already suggested in chapter 6 that our understanding of prayer, and the reasons why it sometimes seems that prayers are answered, may not be due to the result of God interfering with the ordinary running of the world according to its natural laws, but may have a simpler explanation which is not supernatural.

So, is it irrational, or absurd, to suggest that there may be a rational explanation for all phenomena which are at present believed to be supernatural?

The fact that we do not *yet* know the natural explanation does not mean that one does not exist. Perhaps all the beliefs in the Immanent God are as unsubstantiated, and as incapable of substantiation, as those in witches.

10

Sin

The word may mean different things to different people: especially to those of different religions. The usual meaning in the United Kingdom is that which is found in the SOED:

> A transgression of the divine law and an offence against God; a violation of some religious or moral principle.

To the Christian sin has two aspects. One is belief in the concept of Original Sin. The other is that there exists a catalogue of specific acts or tendencies which constitute sins; in particular, the so-called Seven Deadly Sins.

The source of the concept of Original Sin seems to lie in a primitive attempt to account for the undoubted fact that mankind's nature does not seem to be one of unalloyed goodness. That observation carries the implication that there exist criteria by which it is possible to judge what is good and what is bad.

The criteria are usually those which are believed to have come from some deity, such as the Ten Commandments from the Jewish Jehovah. Original Sin is commonly believed to have arisen from the idea that, at some early stage of Man's existence, as in a Garden of Eden as described in the Book of Genesis, he was morally perfect; and that, since then, he has acquired all the bad behaviour which seems to be widespread throughout the species. In the Jewish tradition this change is marked by the banishment of Adam and Eve from the Garden of Eden after they disobeyed God's injunction not to eat the fruit of the Tree of the Knowledge of Good and Evil.

Darwin's teachings about evolution have led us to understand that we were not created immaculate at some specific point in time but are instead the product of generations of change and generations of a struggle for survival. That struggle has made it essential for mankind to have certain traits without which he could not have survived. To what extent those traits can be said to be wholly genetic, and to what extent cultural, that is to say, learned and then passed on to succeeding generations, is difficult, if not impossible, to assess. What history teaches us is that, despite our grouches about what some people are like today, improvement is possible.

It has not yet emerged whether the acknowledgement in 1996 by Pope John Paul, that we are descended from primates, affects the attitude of the Vatican to Original Sin. It is difficult to see how, if Darwin is correct, there can ever have been an era of moral perfection; i.e. that of a Garden of Eden. Perhaps that belief too must succumb to the advance of knowledge.

With regard to the Seven Deadly Sins, I suggest that the underlying nature of each of them is something which cannot be called immoral, or contrary to any God-given law. Each of those sins is, at bottom, a trait which is either essential to survival, or valuable to the community. What makes it anti-social and, consequently, something which is rejected by the community, is that such a trait becomes a sin when it is carried to excess or, perhaps, when it is employed in a context which is harmful to the community.

Let us look at them in turn.

Lust. What is this but excessive sexual appetite or sexual appetite indulged in when the other party does not consent? The point is made in that one sentence. The sexual urge is basic to reproduction in all species which use sexual reproduction: without it we would not be here to consider whether that necessary urge can lead to conduct which can be regarded as a sin. It is the excess or lack of consent which condemn lust.

Gluttony. This is the vice of excessive eating, according to the SOED. Hunger is essential: without it we would overlook the need to feed ourselves. Again, that is a trait which is vital to survival. It is the over-indulgence which causes it to be frowned upon.

Envy. The SOED gives 'a longing for another's advantages' among several definitions. That is the sense in which it is generally used nowadays. Competitiveness is a socially valuable trait because it helps us to do our best in a given situation.

There is nothing anti-social in having the desire, or the will, to improve one's position; nor to do something better than it is done by another person. If there is any possibility of wrongdoing, it would lie in the means used: in other words, in the method of competition, not in the end desired.

Pride. This word is used in two senses: one is an overweening opinion of the excellence of one's own qualities: the other is a consciousness of what is befitting to oneself, such as pride in a neat appearance, or in one's position; such as when a soldier's pride in his regiment leads him to keep his kit immaculate. The second is certainly a quality which is to be admired and is of benefit to the community, or to that part of it, in which such pride is shown.

As to the first, the adjective 'overweening' is what makes the trait unwelcome. It is proper to have a balanced awareness of one's qualities: without it, one may fail to make as large a contribution to the wellbeing of the community as one is, in fact, qualified to do.

Wrath. The SOED calls this vehement or violent anger; also, perhaps surprisingly, righteous indignation. It is not easy to see how this could ever be a sin. What is really important is the subject-matter against which the anger is directed. If that is something which is inimical to the interests of the community, the wrath would seem to be positively beneficial.

Sloth. This is best understood through the word slothful: indisposed to exertion. Nobody should object to the idea of taking a rest when it is proper to do so. Jesus is reported as saying that the Sabbath was made for man; which seems to be in agreement with the last sentence. Sloth arises if laziness is shown when exertion is needed

Avarice. In the SOED: the inordinate desire of getting and hoarding wealth. The words 'inordinate' and 'hoarding' are the significant ones. The getting of wealth, in the sense of creating it, not of stealing it, is beneficial to the community. If anything unacceptable could be involved, it would be in the means used to satisfy the desire; or the keeping of wealth to oneself in an unproductive form, rather than putting it to work. The modern economist might think that Jesus should have told the rich man to put his wealth to work rather than to disperse it by selling it and giving to the poor.

There is a sense in which this sin, in the general form called Greed, is really the root cause of many of the problems brought about by modern man. It has two aspects.

First is his use of this planet and its resources in ways which provide immediate, but unsustainable, gratification of his desire for wealth and good living. He is using up rapidly such irreplaceable resources as fossil fuels; and causing global warming in the process. And he is destroying such vitally important assets as forests.

Greed has another important aspect: the desire to see to one's own wellbeing in disregard of obligations which one may have to other people. This would seem to be the cause of the unacceptable behaviour of those politicians, dictators and the like who disregard the wellbeing of the ordinary people whose servant they are supposed to be; and who instead use their political and military power to feather the nests of themselves and those who are bribed to support them. Names such as Mugabe and Myanmar come to mind. The greed is not limited to them. It is also what drives those who support them: people such as soldiers and police who can lead a good life by ill-treating the ordinary public and living the life of Riley. The ordinary public have no way of fighting back, because they do not have the necessary weapons with which to combat those armed soldiers and police.

Do those of us who are not so encumbered have a duty to help? If we do are we interfering where we have no right to? And if we fail to do so are we guilty of Sloth?

The concept of Original Sin still seems to be alive in some places. When it is mentioned, it is usually in a context which states a need for the assistance of the Christian God, if it is to be overcome. This is akin to saying that mankind cannot, by taking thought upon the matter in question, either form his own view of what should or should not be done, or devise better ways of conducting his affairs.

Not only is this a defeatist attitude, it also completely fails to recognize what mankind has achieved in recent years; and achieved both in a context of religions other than Christianity, and in a context of no religion at all.

Such achievements include a recognition that war ought never to be an instrument of policy; a recognition of the vulnerability of our planet and the need to protect it; an objection to the use of child labour, especially for long hours in arduous conditions; a recognition of the need to create wealth, and to balance that with the desirability of using it for the avoidance of poverty; a concern to attempt to rehabilitate criminals so that they may become useful and agreeable members of society.

There is much more that one could add to the list. What is plain is that such views were not held two or three centuries ago. When regard is had to the fact that Christianity has been around for a lot longer, it is difficult to attribute these changes to that particular religion or to its teachings. Nor is it easy to attribute them to prayer to any particular God, or to any God at all. If they have been brought about by the unsolicited efforts of a God, one is entitled to ask 'What kept you so long?'.

I suggest that the explanation is that mankind has acquired, in recent years, much more knowledge about himself and his environment; and has begun to develop something, however little, of a quality of empathy: that ability to perceive the world as it may be seen through the eyes of others.

So far as concerns learning about his environment, it is beyond question that that knowledge comes entirely from the continued study of his environment through the principles of scientific examination. As to himself the increased knowledge comes partly from the study of his behaviour along the same principles, and partly from the fact that modern communications and travel have forced upon each of us an awareness of other cultures, and the differences from our own.

This is not to say that everything is now satisfactory. Far from it. We still have murders, muggings, burglaries, riots, police brutalities and much more. Perhaps the worst of all, we have terrorism. Much thought and debate is going into understanding the causes of these phenomena and finding cures for them. How is progress to be made? Will the concept of Original Sin help in that progress? Or is progress more likely to be made by examining the details of our social structure; asking ourselves what are the possible causes of the phenomena we see; taking such steps as we can to test which of those possible causes is the more likely to be responsible; and then altering affairs to eliminate or change them?

A recent development in this area has caused consternation among some people. It has been postulated that certain individuals may possess in their genetic make-up genes which predispose them to be anti-social, and consequently predispose them to commit crimes. The knowledge of the detail of our genes and what they do is still at such an early stage that it is not possible to say whether this is a real possibility or not.

It is nevertheless a possibility which cannot simply be dismissed. Our knowledge about human behaviour and its causes has advanced in ways which were not foreseeable even a few years ago.

In Biblical times, one who was regarded as 'mad' was believed to be possessed by a devil; as the tale of the Gadarene swine suggests. Today, we recognise many different forms of mental illness and are aware of the causes of many of them. We have also found methods of treatment for some of them. We have, quite recently, learned that genetic defects can be the cause of diseases.

It has also been asserted that there are cases where traits of a beneficial kind can be traced to genetic make-up. In some species there occurs a phenomenon which appears to be altruism, such as among certain birds whose feeding of young is contributed to by birds which are not the parents. The regular occurrence of this behaviour in those species argues for a genetic basis for it. More directly, it has been reported that a certain hormone makes the American prairie vole into a devoted father compared to other voles. The presence of such hormones in the blood stream, and the centres upon which they operate, are both dictated by the creature's genetic make-up.

We are at the beginning of learning about and understanding such things. We are also at the beginning of understanding to what extent our own behaviour may be affected by our genetic make-up. It is not impossible that it will emerge that some of us do have genes which predispose us to certain forms of conduct which, in the form of society in which we live, are anti-social.

The problems which this may pose have been discussed by, among others, Dr.Habgood, Archbishop of York, in *The Times* of 24th July 1993. He has seen that such revelations will require us to rethink our attitude to anti-social behaviour and to question our present views as to how far the individual should be held responsible for his behaviour. But, as he says, we must beware of the extreme views: that nobody is to be blamed for his wrongs, because his genetic makeup is the cause; and that a person is always to be blamed for what he does, regardless of his genetic makeup. What is really at issue here is whether such an individual should be punished for anti-social behaviour; or whether some other course should be taken.

This dilemma is not a new one. As long ago as the 19th century the House of Lords was faced with the question whether a murderer. named McNaughton, should be held guilty if he was mad.

They said that the question to be answered was whether he was suffering from such defect of the mind as not to know what he was doing, or not to know that what he was doing was wrong. The difference between that approach and today's lies in two things: the recognition that the inability to know may be due to genetic make-up before birth, rather than disease of the mind subsequently acquired; and the concept that such make-up may conduce to anti-social behaviour without going as far as not knowing that one is doing wrong.

The consequence when such a one as McNaughton is found not to know is that he is held 'during Her Majesty's pleasure': a phrase which means that he is kept in prison or hospital until, if ever, he becomes sane again. If we are to adopt the genetic defect approach to all crimes or anti-social behaviour, we will have to consider what to do with people who are, for the genetic reason, found unable to go 'straight'. Will it be necessary, and acceptable, for us to incarcerate them, in a prison or hospital, until some supervisory body can assure us that they have been cured of their defect and can be allowed among the public without a risk of repetition?

Such proposals may seem extreme today, but we may have to take serious notice of such individuals. Indeed, we are already being faced with this problem in the field of paedophilia and similar sexual deviations. All too often, such people seem to suffer from such a mental disorder that, if they are imprisoned and released after their sentence, they re-offend. We have proposals to put the names and faces of such people on the internet; to fit them with some form of electronic tagging; to publicise their names and addresses in the neighbourhood in which they live. But there is no doubt that we have a problem.

It used to be generally believed that, when a criminal had served his sentence, he was entitled to be treated as having redeemed himself and as being entitled to be treated as any ordinary citizen.

Are we right to apply this approach to a habitual paedophile, or a habitual thief, or should we accept that protection of the public demands that such people be kept where they cannot do harm: either permanently or until declared harmless? Should our law be altered so that, for certain crimes, the Court does not prescribe a sentence in prison, but orders that the criminal be incarcerated in a prison or hospital until he is fit to rejoin the public? We already do this with murderers who are held to be of unsound mind. Should we apply that principle more generally?

Interestingly, until some time after World War II, we had a penal provision in our law which allowed a habitual criminal to be sentenced to Preventive Detention. This meant that he was kept in prison for the time specified by the Judge, or until the Probation Service decided that he had mended his ways to the point where he could safely be released among the public without risk of re-offending. There seems to be a need for this today, but the overcrowding of our prisons makes it impractical. And it would be argued by some that that would be an interference with their Human Rights.

As we learn more about ourselves, the need to steer a sensible course between the extremes to which Dr.Habgood refers, will become more important. It can only be to our advantage to learn, if it be the fact, that certain individuals are predisposed by their genetic make-up to be anti-social; and in what respects

92

they are so disposed. With such knowledge, remedial action may become possible; perhaps by teaching, by medication or by some other as yet uninvented means. If cure is impossible, the question will arise whether we should take steps to protect the public, instead of treating the criminals in such a way that they are able to inflict themselves on the public again.

However that may develop, belief in the concepts of sin, and of Original Sin, which were mankind's early ways of attributing a cause to mankind's anti-social behaviour, no longer seem to be appropriate. That belief has been displaced by the growing knowledge of the reasons for such behaviour.

* * * * *

There is one aspect of what some Christians consider to be Sin which has given rise to great conflict between different sections of believers.

There are many Christians to whom practising homosexuality is anathema and who are apparently prepared to leave the Anglican Community because of their beliefs.

It is public knowledge that, in USA, there are priests, and even bishops, who admit to being 'practising homosexuals'. Those words are in quotes because of their ambiguity. What has never been baldly stated is whether that phrase refers to men who are sodomites; that is to say, who practice what is sometimes referred to as 'anal intercourse'.

That practice is condemned in the Bible as sinful. There are some who take that condemnation to mean that any practitioner is guilty of an unpardonable sin.

Whatever may be the pros and cons from a purely theological point of view, it cannot be overlooked, for the reasons explained in Chapter 3 that, even if homosexuality is really genetically driven, it is caused by a genetic aberration and cannot be regarded as a trait which is natural to a human being.

11

Fundamentalism

The SOED defines that word as:-

> Strict adherence to orthodox tenets (e.g. the literal inerrancy of Scriptures) held to be fundamental to the Christian Faith.

Such adherence is contrasted in the definition with liberalism and modernism. Fundamentalism, in the above sense, appears to have started in USA as a reaction against the spread of liberalism and modernism; these were the movements which sought to reinterpret the Bible in the light of modern knowledge. In other words, members of those movements were prepared to examine their beliefs and debate whether they could or should be modified in the light of facts which had been discovered since those texts were first written.

Today it is recognised that such strict adherence is not confined to the Christian faith, nor to the USA, but can be found in all faiths and all countries.

In particular, this belief that the original words of the original sacred text can only mean exactly what they meant when they were written, and are not to be re-interpreted, has been shown by many Muslims. Many of them will assert that the Koran is the word of God and that it means, and means only, that which it meant in the seventh century: that it cannot be subjected to exegesis. This belief has led some of them to perpetrate acts of violence which have not been seen except in wartime.

Examples of such acts are the hijacking of airliners with people on board and flying them into the World Trade Centre towers in New York on 11th September 2001; the bombing of buses and Underground trains in London in July 2005; bombing by the suicide bombers of Palestine; and the destruction of the mosque at Ayodyha in north India. The first three were the work of Muslims and the last the work of Hindus.

Such strict adherence to ancient belief was shown by Pope Pius XII in 1950 when he was still asserting, almost a century after Darwin's work was published, that Darwin's ideas were just a theory; and that the Catholic doctrine, based on Genesis, that God created mankind, as a separate deliberate act, contained the literal truth. He, too, was a fundamentalist.

Long before 1950, the scientific community had accepted that mankind had evolved as Darwin proposed and that the words of Genesis should not be taken literally. Whether the words of Genesis were spoken to a prophet by God, or represented the considered thoughts of those of ancient times who could perceive no other way in which the world and mankind could have come into being, is not important. What is important is the fact, which ought to be obvious to all, that if God had set out to explain to such a prophet, or to mankind generally, the concepts of the Big Bang, of Quantum Mechanics, of electromagnetism and of evolution by Natural Selection, nobody could have understood a word, because the underlying scientific knowledge had not then been uncovered.

Suppose instead that those words of Genesis were spoken to a prophet by a God who knew how it all really happened (because He was personally responsible for the existence of the Universe) such an action is consistent with the experience of every parent who has to answer his child's questions. Some questions have to be answered in an allegorical or similar way, because the child lacks the basic knowledge necessary for an understanding of a full, accurate and complete answer to the question.

As we grow up we learn that Santa Claus does not ride around the sky with a sledge full of toys pulled by reindeers and bring the toys down the chimney at Christmas; nor does the Tooth Fairy take the tooth from under our pillow and leave a coin in its place. Most of us have no difficulty in appreciating that we can be told, and believe, things as a child which we later find out are not true. So it was with the two Popes and Darwin's concepts. So it should be with everyone who finds conflict between what is written in holy texts and what has been learned in the many hundreds of years since those texts were first promulgated.

Many examples have been mentioned in earlier chapters of instances where theological dogma of bygone days has been replaced, in the minds of the theologians themselves, by a recognition that such dogma is no longer tenable. In this respect, there is a parallel between the change of view as a child grows up and the change of view as our knowledge of our world increases. It can safely be asserted that such knowledge will continue to grow; the minds of theologians need to be aware of this. They must be ready to abandon that which is no longer tenable. They should be ready and willing to accept the secular view rather than resist it.

The 'Creationists', who originate from the mid-west of USA, furnish an example of people attempting to resolve a conflict between their fundamentalist beliefs and the powerful arguments presented by the facts discovered by scientists. They have invented a kind of discipline which they call 'Creationism' and which purports to use the language and approach of science as a means of justifying a belief that Genesis sets out the actual process by which God created the world and mankind. More recently, they have been using a phrase 'Intelligent Design'; but without deigning to tell us who the Designer is.

One of the approaches which they use is to argue that there are many complex details found in biology for which the detailed analyses of evolution have not, or more accurately not yet, found an explanation. This, they contend, is proof of 'intelligent design' and therefore of the fact that evolution cannot explain everything.

Their efforts run into countless problems where either their beliefs conflict with what science has discovered, or where they are unable to provide a rational and consistent explanation of much of what we know. This is not the place for setting out all the weaknesses of Creationism but it may be worth noting some of the more glaring failures of their approach.

The world is strewn with evidence of happenings for which neither Genesis, nor indeed the whole Bible, can account; but which are happenings for which the evidence is now over-whelming.

Examples are the age of the Earth as indicated by radioactivity; movement of the tectonic plates; the expansion of the Universe;

the presence of innumerable fossils in layers which have been reliably dated, such as the early bacteria, the trilobites and the dinosaurs.

To suggest that God 'planted' these things makes a mockery of Him.

The efforts of the Creationists to establish their 'science' have not caused any lasting harm, although they may have resulted in some young people being misled into beliefs from which it may be difficult to wean them when they are older. There have been efforts to require school boards in the USA either not to teach evolution, or to teach 'Creationism' as well. For the most part they have failed.

Then there is this puzzle. The Creationists are mostly Christians from the Midwest of the USA. So far as we can tell from the Gospels, Jesus did not regard what Genesis had to say about the Creation as being of central importance. He was a good Jew and recognised what we know as the Old Testament as the sacred Jewish book that it is. Why then do those Christians attach so much importance to believing that what that old Jewish book said about Creation is historic truth? Is that part of Genesis more than a piece of Jewish folklore? Does it have anything to do with what Jesus taught?

The story of Abraham and Isaac referred to in Chapter 4 is worth a mention here because it illustrates Islam's preoccupation with acceptance of the strict fundamental meaning of old texts; in contrast with the exegesis which the more thoughtful people of the world have brought to bear as the knowledge of humankind about their world has progressed.

Abraham is highly regarded by Islam. Muslims have a festival called Eid-ul-Adha which commemorates that incident: apparently on the ground that it shows Abraham's willingness to obey Allah's will; even to the point of killing his own son.

Does not this place God's desire for instant obedience higher than His attitude to killing as revealed so clearly to Moses? Surely, God expected Abraham to refuse and to say 'I will not kill. Do with me as you will, but I will not kill'. Was not Allah dismayed by Abraham's craven subservience? And did He put the ram there to save Isaac from his father's folly?

97

This fundamentalism of the Islamist terrorists has had most serious consequences. On 11th September 2001 the twin towers of the World Trade Centre in New York were destroyed, as was part of the Pentagon, and thousands of people were killed, by Islamic fundamentalists, by whom self-immolation was considered a privilege blessed by God. Such acts are condemned by many Muslims as being contrary to the Koran. Nevertheless, there are many Muslims, including many clerics, who have their own views of what the Koran says and means, and by whom such behaviour is considered right and proper.

What is perhaps worse is that the young people who do these deeds at the behest of the clerics are programmed into believing that their acts will be approved by Allah (despite the Koranic injunction not to kill); and that they will go to Paradise where each of them will have 70 houris for their pleasure. To say that that is worse than believing in Santa Claus is putting it mildly.

There is, indeed, every reason to infer that the Islamic terrorists are conducting a war against the free world, and against all forms of logical analysis of the world. It seems that they are 'hell-bent' (an appropriate phrase) on undermining the whole of the ethos of the free world, of secular thinking and secular laws, of democracy, of freedom of thought and action, and of the emancipation of women; that their serious aim is to control the world on a supposedly Koranic basis, employing Sharia law. Their beliefs are in head-on conflict with the knowledge which has been so arduously struggled for over the centuries since Mohammed. It is not an exaggeration to say that these Islamists are a danger to the free world, and one which the free world has not yet fully appreciated.

To return to Christianity, in recent times the texts on which the Bible is founded have been subjected to study from many points of view and, in particular, contrasted with information derived from other sources, such as contemporary historical records. The result has been to cast doubt on many statements which the Bible contains.

To the scientist, every religious text lays itself open to such study and comparison, be it the Bible, the Koran, the Bhagavad Gita, the Vedanta or anything else. What distinguishes the fundamentalist is his refusal to accept the possibility that the text ought to be subjected to such study and reinterpretation. To him, the text is set in stone; it means today what it meant hundreds of years ago; it will always have that same meaning; and any proposition which is not in agreement with that meaning is wrong. They seem to take the view that, although their God has given them a brain, he does not wish them to use it.

It is this set of the mind which makes the present day fundamentalist into a person who will do things, which might have been regarded as acceptable in societies of days gone by, but which are not compatible with modern concepts of freedom and responsibility.

The acts of the fundamentalist Muslims referred to above make it particularly important to understand what is involved in their thinking. Even at the time of Mohammed, there were those who regarded Mohammed as God's last and final prophet, and the Koran as God's last and final instruction to the human race. To suggest to them that the Koran might be the subject of exegesis was wholly unacceptable. What is more, they regarded, and regard, the Koran as requiring them to convert the entire world to Islam because they believe that that is what God requires.

Furthermore, they believe that that must be a conversion of all law, including all secular law, to Sharia law, not merely a changing of religious law

There is no doubt that those who today perpetrate such acts as those of 11th September have the same mind set. To them the culture of the scientific West is wrong; and every effort must be made to bring down the Western culture and replace it with that of the Koran.

To put it another way, such people are as convinced of their rectitude and their need to destroy those who oppose the strict enforcement of their religion as was the Roman Catholic Church at the time of the Inquisition.

On a less serious level, it is interesting to look at the words of a well-known Anglican hymn from Victorian times which begins 'All things bright and beautiful'. The words of the third verse were doubtless considered proper when written. But one does not hear them in Church today because the last couplet is no longer considered to accurately represent the nature of their God's works:-

> The rich man in his castle,
> The poor man at his gate,
> God made them, high or lowly,
> And ordered their estate.

Inherent in the last two lines is the old belief that the King is such by God's will and that the position of everyone in society has been determined by God: with the result that any attempt to change such things is wrong. Such thinking is not so very different from the thinking of those Hindus who believe that it is by holy decree that Brahmins and the Untouchables hold the respective positions in society which are assigned to them.

Ghandi tried to free the Untouchables from being condemned to their lowly position, but without success.

However, there is reason to think that the horrific acts of the more militant fundamentalists are not driven solely by religious belief; but also by a feeling that those against whom the acts are directed are responsible for the oppression of believers of the faith to which those fundamentalists belong. One example of this attitude of mind is found among the suicide bombers of Palestine. They hold the view that Israel has wrongly invaded and annexed land which rightly belongs to the inhabitants of Palestine. The Palestinians are militarily too weak to retake that land and see the future as one of permanent occupation by the Israelis. This is not the place to debate the rights and wrongs of such views. But such views, if strongly held, will clearly make it extremely difficult to change the minds of those suicide bombers away from the fundamentalist beliefs which make it possible for them to commit themselves to such conduct.

It has also been suggested that the events of 11th September 2001 were influenced by the fact that modern communications have illuminated the great disparity of wealth between the rich and the poor of the world; and thereby provided a driving force for trying to shock the wealthy into doing something to reduce the disparity. To acknowledge that possibility is not to condone the conduct; but to recognise that more may need to be done than simply to change the programming of the minds of those fundamentalists.

Human beings are capable, regardless of religion, of recognising that circumstances may make death inevitable and of accepting that inevitability. One example is the military rearguard of a retreating army which will accept the order to fight on and not surrender in order to help save the rest of the army. However, such an attitude of mind is not driven by any fundamentalist belief but solely from a sense of duty towards one's fellow soldiers.

There is plainly an enormous task ahead of us if we are to persuade the fundamentalists that their beliefs are misplaced; and that the facts learned by the scientists must be taken into account when studying texts, however holy, which were written when mankind's knowledge of this Universe was so much less that it is today. Some among us take the view that that is an impossible goal; that these Islamists are so convinced that they are right, that they cannot be swayed by any argument, but will continue to act to undermine our way of life regardless of what we may say or do. If they are right, war may come: indeed some of such people say that we are already engaged in a war with them.

That is plainly a daunting task so far as concerns the Islamic fundamentalists but, until it is done, as it has been to some extent with the Roman Catholic Church, it will not be possible to separate religious and secular matters in their minds, and not possible to wean them away from a mind-set which believes that they have a duty to do what they are at present doing.

12

Life & Death

There are a number of topics which call into question mankind's right to exercise the power of life and death.

Strictly speaking the word 'right' should only be used in respect of the relationship between a course of action and the rules of a community. Membership of a community involves being governed by what the community, or those who exercise power on its behalf, permit a member to do, or forbid him from doing. It is not, for example, correct to speak of 'animal rights'. This is not pedantry. The issue involved in that phrase is not whether the animals have rights; they are not members of the community and cannot have rights in the community. The issue is whether the rules of the community should forbid or permit certain conduct in relation to animals. Consequently, it must always involve a debate as to whether the rules should be changed so as to prohibit members of the community from doing that which was formerly not forbidden; or release them from the prohibition of that which was formerly forbidden. And that, in turn, involves consideration of the balance between what someone is proposing as an 'animal right' and what we may think is best for the humans who are members of that community.

A much more important aspect, of that same problem of what the community should permit or forbid, arises in respect of such topics as euthanasia, contraception and abortion.

Before we get into the details of those matters, let us look at an important aspect of the history of this planet. Until mankind came along, and still in all affairs not touched by mankind, this was a peaceful planet except for one characteristic which seems to be common to most living things: that is the characteristic of getting food by consuming some other living thing. This characteristic is not confined to such creatures as carnivores. It is only those living things which rely entirely on photosynthesis for energy that are free from this characteristic.

Thus we can see that grasses, vegetables, trees and bushes live by getting energy from the sun, and the raw materials for their structure and metabolism from the air and the soil. They do not need to kill and eat in order to live.

Everything else is, in a loose sense of the term, a predator: it lives by consuming some other living thing. We do, in fact, recognise this in our use of the term 'the food chain'. We are aware that, because of this food chain, a material such as a poison can be eaten by creatures at the bottom of the chain, and passed on up the chain so that we ingest the poison. This characteristic is possessed by all animals, including birds, since they eat grass or seeds or nuts or leaves off trees; by bacteria which have to live by ingesting the medium, usually a living one, in which they live; by funguses which live on things which once lived but are now dead; and by the carnivores.

Until mankind came along, this system of living on other things was a stable one. It changed over the millennia as Darwin has explained, but the changes were slow and gradual except when an incident, such as that which caused the end of the dinosaurs, occurred.

Generally speaking, creatures which live on other things only do so to the extent necessary for them to live. Some creatures, e.g. domestic cats, will apparently kill when not hungry. A lion, however, will kill a wildebeest for food, but will kill no more until it is hungry again. Such living and killing was, and is, effected by members of one species killing and eating members of a different species.

There was, and is, an ecological balance in these matters. If a species eats too much of the available food supply, Darwin's rule of natural selection will restore the balance. As an illustration of what can happen: if a herd of elephants grows too large for its territory, it may strip the trees bare of foliage, thereby kill the trees and bring starvation to the herd. Numbers of elephants then die. So the trees can recover. And so, eventually can the size of the herd.

Members of the same species did not and do not, in general, kill one another. Members of the same species fight each other for territory, which is important for food, and for a mate or harem at mating time. However, it is unusual for such fights to result in death. The vanquished usually runs away and hopes to do better on another day: the victor seldom pursues him, but lets him go.

The species Homo Sapiens behaves very differently. He will fight and kill members of his own species when it is not necessary for him to do so either for food or to get a mate. Indeed, he is capable of doing so on a vast scale and for reasons which have no relevance to his survival on the planet. Like the other animals, he is capable of so depleting the resources which he needs for survival that he exposes himself to the risk of running short of food. However, his talent for invention has so far enabled him to manage to survive despite his depredations on the planet's resources.

The evolutionist will consider that these characteristics, both of living things at large, and of mankind in particular, are the result of mutation and natural selection: the theist may say that they are something deliberately imparted by God. The resolution of that debate has a bearing on euthanasia, etc. If those characteristics are the result of evolution, it is difficult to see why considerations concerning God should be taken into account in relation to such a topic as euthanasia. If those characteristics have been deliberately imparted to us, and to other creatures, by God several problems arise.

One problem is whether the existence of those characteristics is compatible with the idea of the Christian God as a God of Love.

Another is whether mankind's killing and eating of animals is compatible with the idea that he has a soul implanted by such a God. The Jewish Bible gets over that problem by expressing the belief that God gave Man dominion over all living things. Another problem arises from the belief that God gave mankind the 'gift of life'; but not the 'gift of death' as well.

Many, if not all, of these problems disappear if one looks at life from a Darwinian point of view. We have effectively eliminated the smallpox virus from the planet. Does that have any theological implications? Is that virus a creature created by God? If so, do we have any right to eliminate it? From the practical point of view, those are absurd questions. Mankind has always assumed the right to eliminate disease. He has always assumed the right to kill and eat animals. The Jewish Ten Commandments said that we should not kill each other but we have always considered it legitimate to kill in self-defence.

It is against such a background as the above that we should consider the three topics of euthanasia, contraception and abortion.

* * * * *

Euthanasia

It is generally accepted that, although the Hippocratic Oath obliges a doctor to do his best for his patient, there may come a time when he should no longer continue to try to keep the patient alive. This was well expressed by Arthur Hugh Clough who wrote in the nineteenth century:-

Thou shalt not kill; but need'st not strive
Officiously to keep alive.

It is against the background of the exceptions to the injunction against killing which we recognise today (e.g. self defence, military action) that we should consider the question of euthanasia. Does not our acceptance of such exceptions to that injunction justify the conclusion that it must be interpreted according to the circumstances in which it comes into question?

The indiscriminate killing of one citizen by another leads, if not checked, to chaos. Hence if a society is to be, even reasonably, peaceful the general rule must be that 'thou shalt not kill'. The wisdom of having this rule is obvious on secular grounds. It does not, today, require belief in a God to make it a general rule: although it seems that it did so require for the Jews at the time of Moses.

Modern medicine has made giant strides since Arthur Hugh Clough wrote the words quoted above. The important ones in this context are the development of drugs which can hold a disease at bay, without curing it, and sometimes at a terrible price of pain to the patient; and the development of intensive care methods and facilities. The result is that there are many patients to whom, through illness, life has become a burden which they no longer wish to bear. In earlier times they would have been dead before they reached such a state.

Another power which modern medicine has given us, is the ability to keep a patient alive for whom there is no prospect of ever being a true human being again because of irreparable brain damage. It is, however, accepted that, for such patients, it is ethically permissible to turn off the life support system and allow them to die.

There are those who do not recognise that the injunction, 'Thou shalt not kill', has exceptions. A Quaker would not take up arms; but he will go into the battle as a medical orderly. He will not kill; but he does not shrink from the risk of death. Such people are in a small minority.

Is it not sophistry to say that there is a real difference between turning off a life support system, and giving to a terminally ill patient, to whom life has become unbearable, something which will end his distress? Many doctors will regard it as proper to give a dose of a pain-killing drug of a size sufficient to suppress further pain and will do so even though they know it is likely to kill and thereby to end the misery.

It should always be remembered that what is at issue here is not whether a person should be compelled to do something against their wishes: but whether a person should be barred by law from doing something which he wishes done to himself. If euthanasia were to be permitted by law, those whose religious or other beliefs would deter them from availing themselves of euthanasia, would remain free to endure as much pain as they wished for as long as they wished.

In 2001 and 2002, two people made applications to the Courts of the UK to enable them to end their lives. Miss B was paralysed from the neck down and kept alive by means of an electric ventilator which caused her to breathe. She wanted it switched off: her doctors refused to do so. The Court was satisfied that she was of sound mind and fit to decide her future. It also decided that that entitled her to refuse medical treatment which, in turn, entitled her to demand that the ventilator be switched off. In due course, it was.

Dianne Pretty was in the last stages of motor neurone disease. She wanted to die but was unable physically to administer a suitable pill to herself. She wanted her husband to give it to her. The law allowed her to commit suicide, or attempt to do so, without a crime being committed. However, to assist someone in committing suicide is a crime. She asked for an order allowing her husband to give her the pill without being prosecuted. Her request was refused all the way up to the House of Lords, even though she was accepted as being of sound mind and free from duress.

Miss B's experience emphasises that our law raises no objection to suicide on moral, or any other, grounds. Ironically, Dianne could have achieved her ends without any law being broken by the very distressing method of starving herself to death. But the merciful method of being given a pill was denied her.

Together these cases point the way to an intelligent law for achieving Dianne's wish. The law about assisting suicide could be modified so that no offence is committed if the Court permits the act. That would enable the Court to satisfy itself that the patient was of sound mind; that there was no duress; and no objection in commonsense for refusing the permission.

So far as concerns its theological implications, such a law should be regarded as innocuous. It would not oblige a member of a religion to make use of it; it would not prevent the hierarchy of such a religion from proscribing its use for its members; nor from excommunicating those who availed themselves of it.

There seems to be a body of opinion which objects to euthanasia, not on any religious ground; nor on the ground that 'unscrupulous relatives or well-intentioned friends' might take advantage of the patient's plight: but, apparently, because some patients have been 'glad to be alive' after recovering from a situation in which they had said that they wanted to 'end it all'.

Such an argument is sophistry. It is accepted without question that an adult of sound mind is both morally and legally entitled to take steps which others may think he might regret; obvious examples are engaging in dangerous sports and joining the Army. One may well be 'glad to be alive' if one follows advice not to do something dangerous which then nearly kills one. But the right to make the choice is of the essence of that individual freedom which our society accords us. And the experience of Miss B shows that this is entirely a matter for individual choice.

The problem with which euthanasia deals is one which has been aggravated by, if not actually created by, modern medicine and it should be treated on that basis.

Of course, there is a need for safeguards, but no problem has arisen in that regard when it comes to turning off a life-support system, and none in certifying a person as dead so that his organs may be donated to some other person. There will be no difficulty in finding safeguards for euthanasia, given the will to do so. A most important consideration will be determining that the patient is mentally competent to make the decision and is not under duress. The two cases referred to above show that the Courts are fully able to decide such a matter.

Again, it must be remembered that what is at issue is the right for a person to choose: not a law which imposes some action upon him.

Contraception and Abortion

Both are concerned with preventing the emergence into the world of yet another living human.

In most secular countries, there is no law against contraception. In some, the overwhelming power of religious factions makes it difficult to obtain the items which are necessary.

In many countries abortion is forbidden, as it was in the UK until the 1950's. Today, it is not forbidden in UK or USA, for example, if performed in accordance with the local legal requirements. Interestingly, there is a strong movement in the USA to make it illegal again as it was until some 20 years ago.

Once again, some biological background is relevant. Most species of creatures have evolved a form of defence against the depredations of those creatures which wish to kill and eat them. Examples are insects which are poisonous and porcupines which are difficult to get at. Doubtless, these systems evolved as Darwin has explained.

One such system is one which may be referred to as fecundity. It is the ability to reproduce in such large numbers that some, at least, will survive to provide the next generation. Thus we find that the wildebeest produces enough young to offset the depredations of lions; and disease-causing bacteria reproduce themselves in sufficient numbers to leave some to infect the next individual, despite the efforts of the host's immune system to destroy them. In the mammals, reproduction is sexual and it is common to find that a number of offspring result from each copulation, e.g. in the mouse. In the sea we find that many more oyster larvae are produced than survive to adulthood.

In most mammals, copulation only occurs when the female is in oestrus. In some this occurs once a year: in others it occurs shortly after the rearing of a brood. Among the primates a different pattern is found. It seems that the bonobo chimpanzee will indulge in copulation even when the female is not in oestrus. And in that respect, as is well known, the human being has a similar propensity. As a species we enjoy copulation and the urge to copulate is very strong.

There has been much debate about the evolutionary advantage of this human characteristic. One possible advantage is that it increases the number of offspring that can be produced. This is especially so when one remembers that the human female is in oestrus every month. This propensity therefore seems to contribute further to the production of large numbers of offspring. Some say that it has other advantages such as pair-bonding between the parents and that this increases the likelihood of the parents staying together to look after an infant; and so help it to survive to adulthood.

What does seem to be beyond doubt is that, in mankind's early days, the numbers of the human race were so few that they survived as hunter-gatherers. For several millennia after that, the agriculture of the day could feed them. Then, not so long ago, we began a population explosion which is still going on.

An important contributory cause to that explosion is what may be compendiously called modern medicine. That is to say, the recognition of the importance of clean water and good sewage disposal; the importance of cleanliness at childbirth in avoiding perinatal mortality; the development of antiseptics; the development of anaesthetics and surgery; the discovery of antibiotics; and much else besides.

All these factors have conduced to a much higher rate of survival of infants than in the past, and to a greatly extended expectation of life. As a result, the population of the world has risen to some 6,000 million. Feeding this multitude is becoming a problem: a problem which was foreseen by Malthus almost 200 years ago. It has so far been staved off to a great extent by parallel improvements in agriculture. However, there is a limit to what can be done, and a limit to the amount of land which ought to be, and indeed can be, devoted to agriculture. Also there are the problems caused by extensive deforestation and by runoff of chemical fertilizers. Irrigation, despite its value, can lead to excessive salinity if prolonged, with loss of fertility; and there is reason to fear a future shortage world-wide of fresh water. Fish stocks can disappear, and are disappearing, due to overfishing. And apart from the question of food, there is the question of overcrowding, of overlarge cities, and of loss of open country.

For all these reasons we have reached a point where the further growth of the world's population must be stopped in order to protect Spaceship Earth. Experience has taught that it will not be stopped by telling people not to copulate. Hence, some other way must be found. It has been found and, indeed, known about for some time. It is contraception. And that word is not used here either in the sense of simple restraint, nor of restraint except at times when conception is supposedly unlikely. It is used to refer to all those methods whether chemical or mechanical which prevent conception or, which may be the same thing to most people, which prevent implantation and subsequent growth of a fertilized egg.

If you accept Darwin's teachings, you will have no difficulty in recognising that the general adoption of contraception has become desirable if not imperative.

If you are a Roman Catholic, you may be told that it is sinful. It is stated in Genesis that God told man to 'Be fruitful and multiply'. Apparently the Vatican holds the belief that God intended mankind to reproduce without limit. This seems to suggest a failure to believe that their God is capable of recognising what overpopulation means and has not bestowed on those who worship Him enough intelligence to know when enough is enough.

The teaching of other religions is not so clear. The Chinese have levied a tax on anyone who has more than one child as an incentive to use contraception.

It is apparent today that the population of the world has reached the point where limitation is necessary. No priest (except possibly in some minor sects) has said that modern medicine as expounded above is sinful, or something to be eschewed. None has said that we should go back to the bad old days of high infant mortality and all the other similar ignorance-based disadvantages which now lie in the past. Nor is it conceivable that any priest would say so. Pope John Paul, who pronounced against contraception, would never have said that.

It is at this point that secular thinking should be permitted to overrule, or bring about a change in, any doctrine, or any voice of 'authority', which refuses to recognise how matters have changed; which refuses to recognise the seriousness of the present state of affairs; and which will not allow itself to weigh up the effects which we face and the causes of, and cures for, them.

Those who raise objection to contraception must ask themselves which is to be preferred – to prevent conception and so

111

prevent a new foetus being formed – or to allow unrestricted population growth with the inevitable poverty, famine, hardship and death which that will cause. In considering this question, no member of any religion, or of any political party or other group, has the right to decide for its own followers without regard to the rest of the world. As John Donne said – 'No man is an island, entire of itself'. And the same must be true of all religions, political parties and other groups in this overcrowded world. In such a context as this, they are not free merely to make it a rule of membership that one should not use contraceptives; regardless of the effect on the rest of the human race. To do so would be to place self above the common good.

* * * * *

The issue of abortion arises in two contexts. One is where, for whatever reason, contraception has not been used or has failed. The other is where the woman was an unwilling party to the act of copulation, e.g. in a case of rape, or sexual abuse of a young girl; or where drugs or alcohol were used to bring about the woman's submission.

All of them are, inevitably, situations in which the woman does not wish the conception to proceed: it may be said that her real wish was either that no copulation should take place, or that conception should be prevented. It seems now to have become accepted in the West that enforced copulation in a marriage is rape. Inherent in that view is the recognition of the right of the woman to refuse to allow conception to occur. Regrettably there seems to be reason to think that Islam still takes the primitive view that a woman has no right to refuse copulation by her husband.

It follows logically, that the question whether or not the woman should have an abortion, is one for her alone to decide. If it is once conceded that she has a right to the use of contraception, the question arises: on what basis can it be disputed that she has a right to an abortion, if that is what she wishes?

Some people, and some religions, raise objection to abortion on the ground that a new human life has been formed at the moment of the sperm enters the egg. Dr.Habgood, Archbishop of York, pointed out in an article in *The Independent* newspaper of 20th April 1995 that that is an unwarranted assumption. A fertilized egg is nothing if implantation in the wall of the uterus does not take place, because without that, it cannot grow. It is also a most serious question at what stage the developing embryo can be said to be human. It goes through many stages in its early days and may even look like a fish. It should never be forgotten that, at the time of writing of the scriptures which are relied upon for Christian views, an embryo had little, if any, chance of surviving at all if it did not go to full term. It is logically inconsistent to use arguments based on the knowledge of that era for judging what should be done in an era when medicine can bring about the survival of an embryo which is only some 20 or so weeks old. A better view would recognise that, at the time of the scriptures, a human being was something which had at least survived to normal parturition.

There are further grounds on which such people and religions can be fairly accused of unacceptable inconsistency. As already noted, approximately one third of all implantations fail to go to normal term. Precisely what happens to those embryos is not important here. What is important is that the Roman Catholic Church is inconsistent in its treatment of embryos. If, as the Pope has said, they are 'human already', does not that Church have a duty, consistently with its beliefs, to treat them as such, even though they be aborted by nature? There is no consistency in requiring some embryos not to be aborted by mankind; but failing to accord proper respect to the 'human nature' of the ones which are aborted without mankind's intervention.

There is another matter which invites one to consider whether there is an unacceptable inconsistency in those who oppose abortion. It is IVF.

The technique of In Vitro Fertilization was explained above in Chapter 3. Its practice usually involves the treatment of several eggs, thus resulting in several embryos available for implantation. However, it is seldom that more than two or three are implanted because, although the success rate is not 100%, it is undesirable to inflict multiple pregnancies upon the mother. As a result, it is normal for a few unwanted embryos to be left over. Usually these are destroyed. In fact, there are complicated laws governing whether they may be kept in deep freeze and used later; and when it is obligatory to destroy them.

IVF is carried out in accordance with the law. When embryos are destroyed, that is done in accordance with the law. The destruction of those embryos is, therefore, not murder. Hence, there is a logical inconsistency in those who campaign against abortion on the ground that it is murder, but do not campaign against that destruction of IVF embryos. In truth, there is no distinction between an IVF embryo and one formed by copulation: both, if implanted and all goes well, will grow into adult humans. The Roman Catholic view that a soul is implanted at conception raises that same difficulty; if God implants one when a sperm enters an egg, does he not implant one in the course of IVF treatment?

To fail to recognise these inconsistencies is another indication that the Evangelicum Vitae is ill-considered. This is not to make a plea for the ceremonial burial of miscarried foetuses or unwanted IVF embryos, but to ask for a recognition of our modern understanding of ourselves and of the true impact of modern medicine; and for a re-assessment of beliefs and dogma in the light of that knowledge. As Dr. Habgood has noted, without implantation, a fertilized cell has no future. On that basis, the 'morning after' abortion pill, which inhibits implantation, does not destroy a human life.

If God does not put a soul in a fertilized egg before implantation, the question arises: when does God implant a soul? Does He do it at the moment of implantation of the fertilized egg in the uterus? That, if true, would get over some of the difficulties, but still leave the problems concerning embryos which are naturally aborted and those involved in IVF but are not implanted.

The law in UK does not allow abortion after the embryo has reached a stage when it may have a prospect of survival outside the uterus. Paradoxically, advances in modern medicine have made such survival possible at an earlier stage than was the case when the law permitting abortion was first passed. This has resulted in pressure from some to reduce the time after which abortion is not legal.

There are some who, in opposing abortion, proclaim that it is right to do so on the ground that abortion is murder. They are mistaken. 'Murder' is a technical legal term. It cannot be applied to a lawful killing. That is why it is not murder to kill in self-defence or in war: nor, in the USA, for those so charged by law to kill a murderer who has been sentenced to death.

However, both in UK and USA, the law permits abortion provided that certain conditions are observed. Such people do not advance their case against abortion by using the word 'murder'. To use plain English, to cause the expulsion of a foetus in circumstances in which that is permitted by law is not murder.

There is one group whose objection appears to be based, not on religious grounds, nor on an objection to abortion as such, but on an objection that it is used as a convenience. This was put by Noelia Garcia of France, in an article in the *Sunday Times* of 3rd December 1995, where she said that it is 'used by a consumer society that chucks away the babies it does not want'. This attack on the 'consumer society' fails to deal with the problem of the population explosion and the appetite for copulation which is its cause. Nor does it recognise the high percentage of conceptions which result in a natural termination, or prevention, of pregnancy. It should always be remembered that, in the Western countries, no woman is forced to have an abortion: it is simply something which is available to those who wish to use it, provided that they use it in accordance with the local law.

Nobody has the right to deny abortion, or anything else, to another solely on the ground that they, personally, have a distaste for it.

If the objection is based on religious grounds, the objection should be confined to those of that faith: the adherents of that faith have no right to impose their beliefs on others, through the secular law. If the objection is based on secular grounds, what are they? The refusal to forbid a woman from having an abortion cannot be justified on the ground of some general consideration which affects the whole community, as can the refusal to tolerate murder. That this is so can be seen from the fact that the use of abortion has not led to any breakdown of civil order in any of the countries which have decided not to forbid it. Where there is objection, such as the extreme behaviour of some people in USA, it flows either from religious beliefs, or from those who wish to assert a right to forbid others from having that which they do not themselves wish to have.

Embryonic Research

First, mention should be made of the potential value to humanity of research into the nature and development of embryonic tissue.

Such tissue is at a stage where cell division, multiplication and differentiation are at a peak. Studies of such tissue hold out the prospect of leading to an understanding of these three activities. When they are fully understood, the knowledge may be expected to throw light on the causes of, and possible cures for, a multitude of illnesses and medical problems, e.g. cancer. This is because a cancer grows by excessive multiplication of cells in an undifferentiated form.

To take an example, if a person gets a liver cancer, the cancerous cells multiply at a rate which is much greater than that of normal liver cells, and do so in a form which is not that of liver cells and which is of no use in the discharge of the functions of the liver. In short, the liver just disappears as a liver. The result, of course, is death; except, perhaps, if a transplant is possible without any risk of re-infection. Those engaged on this work believe that many other benefits, e.g. repairing a damaged spinal cord, may be made possible by developments from such research.

It is convenient to deal here with embryonic research, because much of the material which those involved in the research propose to use comes from aborted foetuses. Such foetuses result from either natural, or induced, abortion and are available for use only if consent is given by the woman who carried that foetus.

Next, it is relevant to remember that there is nowadays a widespread practice of using organs from deceased persons, as replacements for use in a person whose natural organ has deteriorated, perhaps to the point where his continued existence is problematical. Such organs include heart, lungs, kidneys, liver and corneas.

Those organs are not taken without consent. Frequently the consent has been given in the form of a 'Donor Card' signed by the donor when in good health. It is usually necessary for the organ to be removed very soon after death, so that it remains capable of surviving in the donee. It is well established that the necessary consent may be given by a parent or by a guardian in the case of a minor. This is particularly the case when the donor has suffered an injury which so damages the brain that recovery from a vegetable state is impossible. In such a case the life support machines are switched off with the consent of the parents or guardian or, in some cases, by an order from the Court giving consent.

No objection has been raised to this practice either as a matter of law, or by any of the principle religions. The inference must be that such practice is not inconsistent with their beliefs. Nor are there any groups of objectors who campaign against this practice as is done against abortion. There are those who would not accept such an implant, just as there are those who refuse blood transfusions; they afford no basis for a general objection.

Since it is accepted practice for organs to be removed from a deceased child, in order to benefit living people, upon the authorisation of a parent, what logic is there in depriving the 'parent' of an unborn child, i.e. a foetus, of the right to allow the tissues of that foetus to be similarly used?

Clearly there is no logic where the foetus is naturally aborted. To make objection where the abortion is induced is really the making of objection to the inducing of abortion itself.

Some people have raised objection to the use of embryonic tissue on the ground that it is unnecessary because there are other human tissues which are just as effective. That proposition is not generally accepted. In any event, it is not an objection which justifies restraining those researchers, who think the embryonic tissue is the best, from using it. The others remain free to use alternatives.

In short, it is illogical and untenable to object to the use of an aborted foetus for research work where the mother has given consent for it to be so used.

The possibility exists, in theory, for embryonic material to be used to make a clone of a human being. That is considered unacceptable in the UK and the law precludes it. If such cloning ever seems likely to become technically feasible, somebody in some other country may well attempt it. If that happens, we shall have to grapple with the problems, both human and religious, which it raises.

Life Support Systems

These deserve a mention in this chapter

At the time of Moses and the Commandment not to kill, medicine was in a very primitive state. If a person was severely injured or suffered from a serious illness, either he would survive or he would die; quite soon in each case. Things were just the same at the time of Jesus.

In recent times, mankind has used his knowledge and ingenuity to devise systems which can keep a patient seemingly alive even when he is "brain dead"' that is to say that he is no more than a chemical machine kept going but with no sight, hearing, thought or feeling; unable on his own to breathe or eat or otherwise do anything for himself. It is sometimes referred to as a vegetative state.

In November 2008, such a case went to the highest Court in Italy. A father wanted permission to turn off the life support system which had kept his son, Eluana Engaro, in a vegetative state for 17 years since he was severely injured in a car crash. He was given permission

The Vatican protested, presumably on a theological basis. I suggest that they failed to think things through clearly, as I suggested over the question of when a soul enters a fertilized egg or embryo.

It is an important aspect of Christian belief that, when a believer dies, his soul goes to a phase of Eternal life.

If Eluana had not been put into a life support system, his soul would have made that journey 17 years ago. What has been the status of his soul while he has been on the life support system? Has it been kept trapped inside an empty hulk until the system was turned off? Or did it leave when he was injured and before he was put on that system? It seems unlikely that there are any other possibilities.

This seems to make the position of the Vatican untenable in Christian belief. Either the system was keeping alive a body from which the soul had gone; or it was keeping Eluana's soul trapped in that hulk and preventing it from starting on its Eternal Life.

Whichever is correct, it is clear that the decision to turn off a life support system should be based solely on secular considerations; that is to say, on the advice of the medical profession. The Vatican ought not to ask it to be kept on longer than that.

13

Was Jesus More Than a Man?

This is a question which may have little interest for Jews, Hindus and Muslims but is central to the beliefs of a Christian.

To the Christian, Jesus was not a mere mortal man: he was the Son of God, the middle one of the Trinity of Father, Son and Holy Spirit and, according to Handel and many others, he was the Messiah.

To the Jew, he was a mortal man and certainly not the Messiah. To the Muslim, he was a prophet in the long line leading from Abraham to Mohammed, who was Allah's last and final prophet; but Jesus was not more than a prophet. To the Hindu he was just another mortal man.

What do we know about him? In the New Testament we have the Gospels, Paul's Epistles and the Acts of the Apostles. We also have various secular historical records which, in recent years, have been much studied and compared with the religious texts. We also have a great deal of knowledge of facts which the human race has learned in the last few hundred years.

Although Matthew tells of the Three Kings and of Herod's slaughter of the children of Bethlehem, and Luke tells of him as a boy having discussions with learned men, very little is heard of him in the Gospels until much later.

Modern knowledge of genetics raises an interesting question. Normally it takes two threads of DNA to make a viable conception – one from each parent. If Mary's conception was Immaculate, what was the state of DNA in the implanted egg? What ensured that the child was male? How much of Jesus's thinking resulted from his genes, and how much was the result of cultural programming? Of course, such questions did not arise at the time; and it is easy to dismiss them today on the ground that because he was the Son of God such questions are irrelevant. Nevertheless, it is said that he was a man which implies that his bodily make-up and functioning were those of an ordinary human man.

One thing is clear; that, in religion, he was an ordinary Jew. At the time and place of his birth he could have been nothing else. The Gospels do not speak of him as trying to establish a new religion aimed at displacing Judaism. In fact, they suggest that he was careful to avoid a conflict with the Jewish religious authorities as is evidenced by the anecdote concerning the adulteress who was about to be stoned to death. If he had said that he approved of that penalty he would have undone much of his efforts in preaching: if he had said he did not approve he would have been accused of blasphemy, with its terrible penalty. He managed to avoid committing himself either way. That anecdote suggests that he knew the Judaic law well.

As to the miracles reported in the Gospels, there is no way of telling whether the reports are historical truth, legend or myth. They were not written down until some 70 years after Jesus's death. It is curious that, although Paul made such great efforts to spread the general ideas which are attributed to Jesus in the Gospels, he does not in the Epistles quote what is quoted in the Gospels, nor place reliance on the miracles reported in the them. There does not seem to be much, if any, indication that Paul was promulgating a new religion as opposed to trying to make Judaism available to Gentiles, whom he regarded as pagan.

The reports of the miracles themselves raise questions as to what really happened. Consider, for example, the tale of the Gaderene swine. No doubt it was common belief at the time that madness was caused by devils. But would not Jesus have thought differently if he was more than a man? Would he not have been able to cure the madness without sending a herd of swine to their death? Since we know today that the madness was not caused by devils, what was it that sent the swine running? Is it not reasonable to ask today whether it all happened as stated?

Then there is Lazarus. How long had he been 'dead'? Was he in fact dead as we would understand it today; or was he in a coma? How long after death would Jesus have been able to raise somebody from the dead? Did Jesus perceive that Lazarus was in a coma? If so, was his act a cynical trick? Or is the story a myth?

There is a general discussion of miracles in Chapter 7.

The view which, as a secularist, I take about the Jesus spoken of in the Gospels is that he was of a similar turn of mind to that of Martin Luther; in that he did not approve of the way in which the Sanhedrin and the priesthood had taken such control of religious dogma and practices that it was difficult for the ordinary Jew to feel that he could make contact with his god. This would seem to be the purpose of the reference to a Phari-see praying in public and an ordinary person praying 'in his closet'. This view is consistent with all his sermons.

Then there is the interesting fact that much of what is reported about him in the Gospels is of a secular, rather than theological, nature as the following illustrate. First, the tale of the adulteress who was about to be stoned. From a theological point of view that was the Jewish law, but Jesus clearly thought that it was not good law. Then there is 'Love thy neighbour', which is not directed at mere thought, or at supernatural matters, but at practical secular action as the tale of the Good Samaritan illustrates.

No secularist would dispute that Jesus existed. There is evidence outside the Gospels which indicates that he was tried and crucified in Jerusalem. But the lacunae in Paul's letters and the long time which elapsed before the Gospels were written justify doubt whether the contents of the Gospels should be taken as historic truth.

Is there any possible rational explanation for what happened when he went to Jerusalem? What is notable is that in the Gospels he is said to have spent most, if not all, of his time before that in the countryside. There he seems to have been acclaimed by the local inhabitants. Perhaps he wanted to try and persuade those who lived in the city of his ideas, despite the risk involved in going there. He seems to have known that he was at risk of a charge of blasphemy for his ideas. The sojourn in the desert and the experience at Gesthemane are consistent with a man who knew that he was taking a great risk and hesitated about taking it.

The Ascent into Heaven raises its own problems because today we know what there is 'up there'. At that time the idea of the Kingdom of God seems to have been something supernatural. What should one have in mind if one was to consider an ascent into heaven today?

It was a gamble which failed. And nobody is likely ever to know what was really going on in his mind.

But the believer will believe despite the available knowledge; and the secularist will doubt because of it.

14

Life After Death

The idea that there is some part of us which lives on after our bodies have died is a very old one. One need go back no further than the Pharaohs of Ancient Egypt. They believed so strongly that there is a life after death that they went to great pains to ensure that they were adequately accompanied for that next world, even to the extent of murdering slaves so that they would be available to serve them.

The world is full of beliefs about life after death, or about the return of a soul to Earth after death. The Reverend Ian Paisley, of Northern Ireland fame, believes, if the media report him correctly, that those who sin will be cast into Hell Fire.

The upper echelons of the Anglican Church have recently been expressing doubts about Hell Fire. They are less sure than they were that a God of Love would condemn anyone to an eternity of such agony: but they continue to believe in life after death. Indeed, it is a concept which figures largely in the Anglican burial service.

According to reports in the media, the perpetrators of 11th September 2001, and the suicide bombers of Palestine and elsewhere, have been brainwashed into believing that they are doing Allah's work and that they will be rewarded by going to Paradise where, among other benefits, each will have 70 virgins as their houris. One cannot help wondering whether even that might pall after a millennium or two. Could they, or would they, be willing to perpetrate such horrors, and to kill themselves, if they were not so persuaded? Such brainwashing is the work of senior members of the Muslim hierarchy playing on the minds of young people who are uneducated, or perhaps so lacking in an aim in life that suicidal bombing does not seem unwelcome.

During the trial of one man accused of terrorist activities, counsel challenged him and said that he had been brainwashed as set out in the last paragraph. He wittily countered by saying that he had had his brain washed by Allah. Perhaps there is merit in the use of the word 'program' used in Chapter 2.

The Norsemen believed there was a place called Valhalla to which they would go. Many Hindus believe that they have a soul which comes back to earth after death. They might, apparently, come back as a dog instead, but they would not welcome that.

How much do we know about what Shakespeare referred to as 'the undiscovered country from whose bourn no traveller returns'?

Very little has been explained about the nature of life beyond Shakespeare's bourn. One of the characteristics of this, our present, life is that of development. We go from being an infant to, if one is fortunate, maturity; and then eventually to death. With the brains which we have, we do not merely exist. Nor do we merely survive; that is to say, feed and reproduce. We do much more.

We work; we design things; we make things; we play bridge or poker, or football or golf; we make friends and enjoy passing our time with them; if we are fortunate we fall in love; and we do an infinity of other things which require the use of our minds. Do we do such things hereafter, or do we have an eternity of – doing what? Do we have our minds; or are we just empty shadows? Do we use our minds? Or what does happen? Does the prospect of existence without the accompaniment of those things of the mind which appealed to us here, including that of personal development, appeal to you?

Have you ever asked yourself: how shall I spend the first 100 years? Most of us do not live to be 100 anyway. So what will you do for the first thousand years? Or the first million?

Science has got some relevant things to say. It is no longer believed that there is a 'life force' which makes us live and which is different from things which are known to science. It is now clear that we are a complicated assembly of chemical molecules and that the force which makes us live is simply the energy derived from chemical reactions.

We know that, to keep us going, our brains must be supplied with chemicals which provide them with energy and, most importantly, with oxygen. Except under special circumstances, our brains will die if deprived of oxygen for four minutes. That is how close to death we are always living. We also know that the brain is incessantly generating electrical pulses and waves of various kinds: even in sleep. When we die, they all stop.

Here is an interesting analogy. If I pass an electric current along a copper wire, a magnetic field will be generated. The existence of this field can easily be demonstrated to anyone. Bring an ordinary magnetic compass near the wire and it will be deflected by that magnetic field. Turn off the current and the compass can no longer detect a magnetic field. Where has the magnetic field gone? Ever since James Clerk Maxwell developed his equations for the interrelationship of electricity and magnetism, scientists have known that that magnetic field does not 'go' anywhere: it simply collapses and ceases to exist. When you snuff a candle, the flame does not 'go' anywhere: it simply ceases to exist.

Here is another analogy, perhaps closer to the issue. We start life with a certain amount of programming built in by our DNA. As we grow and are subjected to the experiences of life, we acquire more and more in the way of programs. We acquire skills, languages, memories, habits etc. All are stored in our brain. Those programs are the things which give us our personality, the things which other people have in mind when they think about the sort of people we are. Is it so far away from reality to call those things the software which exists in the hardware of our brains? Such a thought is compatible with the fact that when our brain dies it is impossible for anyone to access our personality any more.

As always, there is a lot more to be learned, but there are similarities between what we know about our brains, with their electrical pulses and waves, and that electric current and those programs. Our personality exists while those pulses and waves are working in our brains. When they cease, our personality is no longer detectable by us human beings. Is it true that, unlike the case of the magnetic field, there is a 'something' which continues to exist but in another 'somewhere'?

The belief that there is an afterlife is ancient; it is dear to the hearts of many people; there is no evidence that it exists; and none that it does not. Is that belief anything more than wishful thinking and self deception?

There is good reason for examining this topic, as is illustrated by the reference to 11th September 2001 and the suicide bombers. In general everyday life, the belief in the existence of an afterlife by one person does not have any impact upon the life of another. But there are times when it does, for example, in the case where the existence of a soul is regarded as having a bearing on whether or not abortion should be permitted.

There are so many different versions of what that afterlife is like that it is difficult to accept that any of them is correct. It is idle to suggest that anything said or written today is going to have any effect on those beliefs in the near future. But it is worth remembering that we have learned a lot about such matters over the centuries as witness the discontinuance of making human, and later, animal sacrifices; of torturing people, and of burning them to death, all for religious reasons.

One interesting question is: what would hold the members of a religion together if they abandoned that belief?

15

Whither Religion?

There has been talk in the media of a seeming resurgence in religious observance. The comparisons are made over short time spans such as a few years. The purpose of the above question here is to take a much longer look. It is plain that, in the developed world, religion does not play so large a part in the life of the community as it did, say, four centuries ago.

This question is not concerned with the issue of theism, or atheism or agnosticism; that is to say, whether or not there is a God. It aims to look at the relationship between human beings and God; to consider the importance of religion in the average person's everyday life; and to consider whether we should expect that belief in gods and their commandments should overrule ideas based on current knowledge.

I have touched upon the size and age of the Universe; and the number of stars in each of its many galaxies. Our Earth is just one small planet next to a common type of star on the edge of a quite common type of galaxy; a planet made of the detritus of a supernova.

It is on that planet that there has evolved a species, which we know as *homo sapiens*. It is a species which has developed intellectual advantages over other species. Unfortunately for the planet and its other flora and fauna, that species tends to have habits which are not consistent with the general well-being of the species; or the planet. There is a general tendency to greed and to ecological irresponsibility.

Against that background, it does seem odd that so many of that species take the view that God has a special regard for their welfare. Is that not rather arrogant? They talk of 'The Will of God'. They believe that God has a particular interest in their well-being; and has set up rules as to how members of that species ought to behave. Some are so convinced of God's interest that they think He has told them to convert all of the species *homo sapiens* to their point of view and to kill as many of them as may be appropriate to ensure that end; we call them Islamic Terrorists.

I am not concerned here with morals. All societies have to have rules to govern interactions between their members. This is as true of the old societies such as the Persians, the Greeks, the Romans, the Norsemen etc., as of the modern societies. Morals are not tied into religions. Some say that Hitler and Stalin were bad because they were atheists (that is really a bad bit of *post hoc propter hoc* reasoning). Were they worse than the Popes who had people burned alive and tortured to death? And remember that those Popes claimed to be Christ's Vicar on Earth.

There are so many paradoxes in these beliefs. I have referred to Abraham whom God told to slit the throat of his son; and that Abraham would have done it but for 'a ram caught in a thicket'. Yet a few years later that same God apparently told Moses that it is wrong to kill. Is one to believe that God changed his mind?

Then God warned Noah that there would be a Flood and told him how to build an Ark; and ordered him to take on board a pair of each of the world's animals. No mention was made of kangaroos.

Paradoxically, God did not warn the 300,000 people who were killed by the Indian Ocean Tsunami of Boxing Day 2004. Nor did He warn those killed by Mt. Pinatubo or countless other disasters.

The above is only a taste of some of the oddities. I say nothing here about the Hindus, who have several Gods, nor about the many other religions. To do so is unnecessary.

I therefore find myself bound to ask: is it credible that the God who made this great Universe is really interested in *homo sapiens* and what he does? Or are all the people who think that way deceiving themselves? We know that ritual has a calming effect on many people; it makes them feel that they belong to something; and that comforts them. As to prayer, I have referred to the Placebo Effect; how much of what is believed to be done by prayer is really a consequence of that phenomenon?

So what are we to think? Can it be right to conclude that religion has a basis in reality; and that God is really interested in what we say or do? Or is religion something left over from our early past when we knew so little about our Universe and ourselves? And should we re-examine all these matters; recognise that morals must live on their own justification for the well-being of all of us rather than on somebody's belief that he knows what God wants; and should *home sapiens* stop trying to escape his responsibilities towards his fellows by looking for help from a source from which it never seems to come?

If you have read this far, you will have seen that there are many areas of human activity which were at one time considered to fall within the purview of religion; and that, over the years, one by one, they have emerged from that and become matters which fall to be regarded in accordance with secular considerations.

A person's beliefs are a part of his culture. They are passed on from parent to child, initially at a very early age, and the child is taught to believe, and really does believe, that those beliefs are set in stone and immutable.

It is useless for those who hold the different religious beliefs to try to establish a sort of universal ecumenism by which all such believers agree together. The pressures of the modern desire for ecumenism seem to have led some people of different religions to say that they are all seeking after God in their own way. Others have been known to say that 'Allah' is simply arabic for God and to infer that Allah of the Muslims is the same God as the God of the Christians. The difficulty with such an approach is that it overlooks the different dogmas and incidents of different religions and raises the question whether there is any such thing as absolute truth about God. Is not everything said about the God of a particular religion hypothetical and personal to the speaker?

I suggest that the only way in which any such common agreement can be reached is by using knowledge rather than belief to resolve disagreement; and that means focusing on secular matters and leaving all non-secular ones to be regarded as the private personal beliefs of the individual.

This is the only foreseeable way in which the many different religions and cultures can exist together in an overcrowded global world. In short, we must struggle to agree on secular matters without reference to religious beliefs and agree to make no attempt to impose religious beliefs on other people.